CHEMISTRY 105

PRINCIPLES OF CHEMISTRY 1

GENERAL CHEMISTRY LABORATORY MANUAL

Acid concentration

Writing Space
Just the write up
Written Questions
+ paragraph

RYAN RICE
CALLIE SCHIEFFER
MICK SAKAMOTO
MICHAEL FINNEGAN
SCOT WHERLAND

WASHINGTON STATE UNIVERSITY
DEPARTMENT OF CHEMISTRY
Pullman, Washington

Star
PUBLISHING COMPANY, INC.

STAR PUBLISHING COMPANY, INC.
PO BOX 5165
BELMONT, CA 94002-5165

Printed in the United States of America

ISBN: 978-0-89863-422-8

71316

TABLE OF CONTENTS

PAGE

LAB SAFETY CONTRACT.. v

GENERAL CHEMISTRY LABORATORY COURSE POLICIES ix

LABORATORY REPORT GUIDELINES FOR CHEMISTRY 105 1

INORGANIC NOMENCLATURE.. 13

STOICHIOMETRY AND CHEMICAL ANALYSIS 21

LABORATORY TECHNIQUES AND MEASUREMENTS... 23

PROPERTIES AND REACTIONS OF ACIDS AND BASES: 35

MOLAR MASS OF A KNOWN ACID.. 43

MOLAR MASS OF AN UNKNOWN ACID 53

IDENTIFICATION OF A METAL.. 55

ENTHALPY OF FORMATION OF AMMONIUM CHLORIDE 65

THE DENSITY OF AIR 75

THE SHAPES OF MOLECULES AND IONS... 81

PREPARATION OF AN IRON OXALATE COMPLEX 89

ANALYSIS OF BLEACH BY IODOMETRY... 93

LIMITING REACTANT... 99

ANALYSIS OF IRON BY OXIDATION-REDUCTION TITRATION 107

APPENDIX A: LABORATORY EQUIPMENT A11

APPENDIX B: LABORATORY TECHNIQUES B1

LAB SAFETY CONTRACT

This safety contract states the lab-safety rules that are to be followed by everyone in order to ensure the safety of the work place for everyone (TA's, students, faculty and staff). Two copies are provided that are to be completed and signed by each student: one should be returned to your TA, and the other retained by the student for use as a guide. The latter should be present in the lab-notebook at all times.

GENERAL RULES

1. Pre-lab assignments are to be completed prior to entering the laboratory. Read all experimental procedures in the lab-manual thoroughly before entering the laboratory.
2. Do not attempt lab work if you are on any medication that could interfere with your ability to function safely in the lab.
3. Consumption of any type of food/drink (beverages, chewing gum, tobacco, etc.) or application and/or use of cosmetics (lip balm, gloss etc.) in the laboratory is prohibited.
4. Hands and pens/pencils are to be kept away from face, eyes, and mouth while using chemicals or equipment. Hands are to be washed with soap and water after performing all experiments, especially before going to the restroom or leaving the lab for any reason.
5. Use of cell phones, radios, MP3 players, and/or headphones is not allowed in lab. Store these with your other personal items in designated areas.
6. Students are required to practice disciplined and responsible conduct at all times when present in the laboratory. Playing around in the laboratory, sitting or leaning on the lab benches, and disorderly behavior are not permitted. Be alert and proceed with caution at all times when in the lab.
7. All written and verbal instructions are to be followed carefully. If you do not understand a direction or part of a procedure, ask your TA (or other supervising figure) to clarify it before proceeding.
8. Students must be supervised at all times while in lab.
9. Only experiments that are authorized by the course instructor and supervised by your TA may be performed.
10. Each student may only execute experiments in the work space designated to them, and must personally monitor their experiments while they are in progress. Do not move the equipment/glassware for personal preference.
11. Observe good housekeeping practices. Work areas should be kept clean and tidy at all times. Bring only your lab manual, lab book, and other necessary materials to the work area. All backpacks, coats, and other personal items must be stored away from benches, fume hoods, and all chemicals, and out of aisles. Keep aisles clear.
12. All work surfaces and apparatus are to be cleaned by the student at the end of each experiment. All equipment/glassware must be cleaned, inventoried and returned (clean and in working order) to its proper location when you are done. Broken or missing items must be replaced through the stockroom.
13. Chemicals and equipment are NOT to leave the laboratory unless their removal has been authorized by the supervising authority.
14. All chemical wastes must be properly disposed of. This includes checking the waste container before any chemicals are added to ensure it has an appropriate label. Waste containers are not to be over filled. Notify the supervisor if the container is full.
15. Fume hood sashes are to be closed when not in use. Fume hood sashes are not to be opened beyond the 18'' mark when in use. Never stick your head into the fume hood.
16. Sinks are to be used only for water and solutions that are permitted by your TA. Mixing of chemicals in sinks is not allowed. Solid chemicals, metals, matches, filter paper, and all other insoluble materials are to be disposed of in their proper waste containers, not in the sink.

PERSONAL PROTECTIVE EQUIPMENT

1. Approved chemical splash goggles must be worn at all times when in the lab. The goggles must seal around the face and have no open holes, *no exceptions*.
2. Contact lenses *should* be replaced with prescription glasses.
3. Dress properly for lab. Clothing must cover all parts of the body between shoulders and toes. Lab coats are required for some courses and highly recommended for all others.
   a. NO bare midriffs or ankles
   b. NO tank tops or low-cut tops
   c. NO shorts, skirts, or cropped pants
   d. SHOES must be closed-toed and completely cover the entire foot. NO sandals
4. Long hair, hanging items (jewelry, hoodie strings etc.), and loose or baggy clothes must be secured.
5. Gloves are available for use when needed and must be removed before leaving lab. Do not handle personal items such as pens with the gloves on.

HANDLING CHEMICALS

1. All chemicals in the lab are to be considered dangerous and used with caution. Chemicals are not to be touched or tasted. If needed, chemicals may only be smelled via the "wafting" method and only after this method has been demonstrated to you by your TA.
2. Labels on the reagent/chemical bottles must be checked thoroughly prior to use or transfer. Only the directed amount should be used or transferred. Unused chemicals must not be returned to their original container. All chemicals must be properly disposed of in the appropriate waste container.
3. All reagent bottles and waste containers must be capped when not in use. Reagent bottles must not be removed from their designated dispensing areas.
4. Flammable solvents must not be used anywhere near a flame.
5. Acids must be handled with care and as directed by your TA. Dilute acids by adding add acid to water, not water to acid.
6. Acids and other chemicals must be properly secured prior to transport from one part of the lab to another.
7. Your TA (or other supervising figure) must be promptly notified of any spills. Clean-up of small spills should be performed immediately as directed by the supervising authority.

HANDLING GLASSWARE AND EQUIPMENT

1. Use the dust pan and broom provided to clean up any broken glass; never handle it with your bare hands. Place all broken glass in the container designated for this purpose (it will be labelled either "Glass and Sharps" or "Broken Glass"). Replace all broken glassware with a new piece from the stockroom.
2. Examine glassware before each use. Never use chipped or cracked glassware. Never use dirty glassware.
3. Fill wash bottles ONLY with deionized water and use it only as intended, e.g., rinsing glassware and equipment, or adding water to a container.
4. Unplug hotplates when they are not in use.
5. When removing an electrical plug from its socket, grasp the plug, not the electrical cord. Hands must be completely dry before touching the plug or switch.
6. Report damaged electrical equipment immediately. Look for things such as frayed cords, exposed wires, and loose connections. Do not use damaged electrical equipment.
7. Do not use a piece of equipment until its proper use is demonstrated by your TA.

ACCIDENTS and INJURIES

1. Report any accident (spill, breakage, etc.) or injury (cut, burn, etc.) to your TA immediately, no matter how trivial the accident or injury may seem.
2. Report fires to your TA immediately.
3. If a chemical splashes in your eye(s) or on your skin, immediately flush with running water from the eyewash station or safety shower for at least 20 minutes. Notify your TA immediately.
4. Know the location of the following safety equipment:
   a. Fire extinguisher
   b. Safety shower
   c. Eye wash
   d. First aid kit
   e. Chemical spill kit

EMERGENCY PROCEDURES

In the event of a fire alarm (a continuous sounding bell) while you are working in the laboratory, immediately turn off any Bunsen burners or hotplates you are using and leave the building by the shortest route as designated by your TA. <u>DO NOT use the elevators.</u> Proceed to the appropriate meeting site with your TA; these sites will be posted in your lab room. You must remain with your TA until you have been dismissed by supervising personnel.

In the event of a serious injury or someone becomes ill, immediately turn off any burners or hotplates and evacuate to the hallway until supervising personnel give you additional instructions. <u>DO NOT leave until you have been dismissed by supervising personnel.</u>

I have read and agree to the safety rules set forth in the chemistry lab safety contract. I realize that I must obey these rules in order to insure my own safety, as well as the safety of others. I am aware that any violations of the contract can result in the removal from the laboratory and loss of credit for the experiment. I also understand that I can be held financially responsible for the laboratory equipment used in this course if I break or destroy an item due to carelessness, neglect, or misuse.

_____   _____
Signature   Printed Name

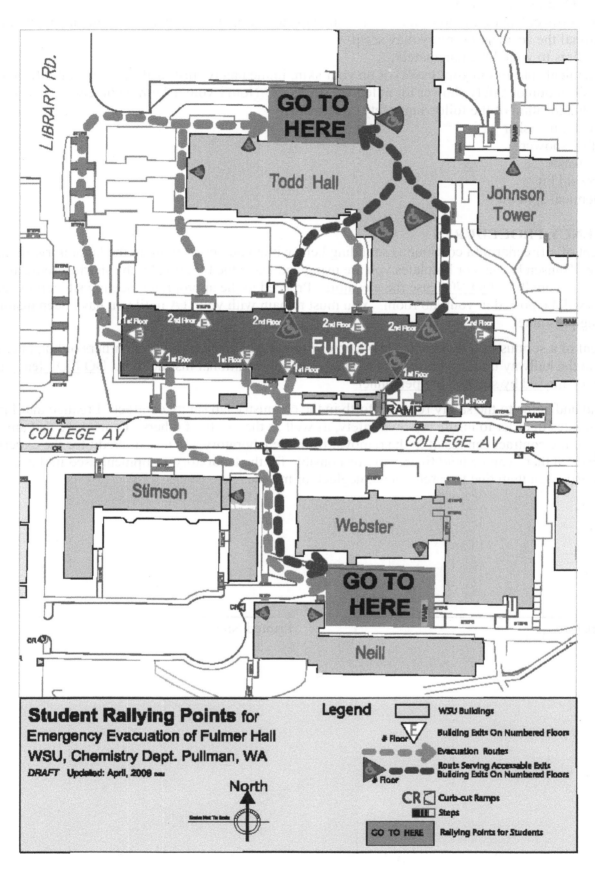

Student Rallying Points for
Emergency Evacuation of Fulmer Hall
WSU, Chemistry Dept. Pullman, WA

DRAFT Updated: April, 2008 nsu

North

Legend

WSU Buildings

Floor — Building Exits On Numbered Floors

Evacuation Routes

Routs Serving Accessable Exits
Floor — Building Exits On Numbered Floors

CR — Curb-cut Ramps

Steps

GO TO HERE — Rallying Points for Students

GENERAL CHEMISTRY LABORATORY COURSE POLICIES

LABORATORY EXERCIES AND REPORTS

This manual contains a selection of experiments and other exercises designed to re-enforce Chemistry 105 lecture topics and develop your laboratory skills. Most of these experiments will be performed during the academic year, but not necessarily in the order listed in the table of contents. Your course syllabus will indicate which lab will be done each week; be sure to check it to ensure you have prepared for the correct experiment.

Each experiment or exercise you perform will have a laboratory report associated with it that you must complete in full. These reports generally consist of three sections that are described in the Report Guidelines chapter of this manual: the pre-lab, the data and observations, and the post-lab. Except as indicated in the Retaking the Course policy description below, you must attend lab sessions and submit a completed laboratory report for an experiment in order to receive <u>any</u> points for that experiment.

You must pass the laboratory part of a General Chemistry class in order to pass the course as a whole.

Late lab reports

If any of the work you are required to submit for a lab report is late, points penalties will be applied to that report. See your course syllabus for details.

If you have any late work (or early work) written on paper you need to turn in, you may submit it to the General Chemistry Office in Fulmer 319A or to your TA. Hand all work to a person; do not slide an assignment under a door.

MISSED AND MAKE-UP LABS

An absence will result in a score of zero for the experiment performed that week unless a make-up is performed (see below). More than two such absences or other grades of zero on a lab report will result in a failing grade for the entire course.

Scheduling a Make-Up Lab

If you are unable to attend your usual lab section in any given week due to illness or a conflicting activity, you may arrange to perform that week's experiment on another day and/or time as a "make-up" lab. Such labs are scheduled exclusively through the General Chemistry Office, Fulmer 319A. Since the times you can makeup a lab tend to be limited and are filled on a first-come, first served basis, it will be to your advantage to schedule the make-up as soon as possible. Each student will only be allowed two make-up labs per semester, regardless of reason.

Make-ups may only be arranged through the General Chemistry Office. You will not be admitted into a make-up lab if you fail to do this.

Although you may attend a make-up lab on a different day than the one you are normally scheduled for, the experiment you perform must be the same one that was scheduled to take place that week; you will not be able to perform an experiment that took place in a previous week.

According to university policy, written documentation for absences due to participation in university sanctioned events must be provided one week prior to the absence. This documentation must be brought into the General Chemistry Office when you schedule your make-up lab, not given to your TA. You will not be allowed to schedule a make-up lab if you fail to follow this policy.

Submitting Work in a Make-Up Lab

When you attend a make-up lab, all course work that would have been due in your usual tutorial and lab periods will be due the day of the make-up lab. The TA of the make-up section will forward your work to your regular TA. The post-lab assignment for the experiment performed in the make-up lab will be due at the same time it is for the rest of your assigned section, even if this affords you less than one week to complete it.

If You Are Unable to Arrange a Makeup Lab

If you are unable to attend your lab session due to an excused absence and can't make it up, you may in some cases obtain data from the course instructor or laboratory supervisor and write your report based on those data. Since these data must be signed by your course professor they cannot be e-mailed to you. You must clearly indicate that the data are not yours in the report. Reports written this way are eligible for a maximum of half of the assigned points for the experiment. The data and post-lab sections of this report will be due one week after your section completed the experiment they correspond to.

RETAKING THE COURSE

Students who are retaking Chemistry 105 may be excused from lab provided their previous laboratory score meets the points-received requirement for this purpose (see the course syllabus for this requirement) and is not more than two years old. In order to be excused from lab, you must report to the General Chemistry Office (Fulmer 319A) within the first week of the semester and obtain written permission. *Such permission will not be granted automatically even if you have a laboratory score that meets requirements.* Students who have been excused from lab must attend all tutorials and are required to do all other assignments that are eligible for points as specified in the course syllabus.

Be aware some lab-related material may appear on your exams, so you are still expected to know and understand it even if you are excused from lab.

Students who are retaking the class and are not excused from the lab must collect data and prepare lab reports for the experiments as if they have never done them before. Resubmitted work will not be accepted.

LABORATORY REPORT GUIDELINES FOR CHEMISTRY 105

The grade you receive for the laboratory portion of this course will depend upon the quality of the reports you submit for each experiment. As mentioned in the Course Policies section above, these reports will generally consist of three main sections: a pre-lab assignment, a data and observations section due at the end of lab, and a post-lab assignment. Pre-lab and post-lab questions/requirements will be provided on-line. Depending on the semester you take this course, you may be required to submit your answers to these on-line or in your laboratory notebook. The data section must be written in your laboratory notebook. You will submit the original pages to your TA and retain the copies in your notebook.

Everything you write in your notebook must be neat and legible. Since you will use the copy of your data to complete your post-lab, you must write hard enough to ensure all of your pen marks, especially decimal points, will appear on the copy. If you make a mistake in your lab notebook, draw a single line through it (~~like this~~) so that the reader can still read the mistake; do not obliterate it by marking through it repeatedly. Do not add something to the copy that is not on the original. Finally, *never use pencil or a felt-tipped pen in your notebook.*

HEADINGS

The first page of your lab data section must have a heading that includes your name, experiment title, date, course and section numbers, and TA name. Your notebook may have spaces at the top of each page labeled for some of this information, but not likely all of it. Make your own spaces or boxes for this information if they are not there already.

All of the other pages of the report must have a heading that includes your name, experiment title, and your section number.

PRE-LAB QUESTIONS

The pre-lab assignment consists of a series of questions that are meant to prepare you for the experiment you will perform. As mentioned previously, they will be administered via an on-line program. Most of the information you will need to address these questions will be found in chapter for the experiment you will perform that week. The remainder will be in one of the appendices in the back of this manual.

Late Pre-Labs

See your course syllabus for your instructor's policies on late pre-lab assignments.

DATA AND OBSERVATIONS

This is the section of your lab report where you will record your data and make your observations. It is also where you will describe the reagents and equipment used, and record a description of the procedure.

Procedure Citation

Each of your experiments must begin with a procedure citation. Since, in most cases, you will follow the procedure as it is given in this manual, you will cite the manual itself. The recommended format for this is:

> The procedure was followed from: Rice, R., Schieffer, C., Sakamoto, M., Finnegan, M., and Wherland, S. (2018) <u>Chemistry 105 General Chemistry Laboratory Manual</u> , Star Publishing, Redwood City, CA; pages __ -- __.

Although most of the experiments you perform will be followed from procedures described in this manual, there may be occasions in which you will be given a handout to follow instead. In this case, your citation will be:

The procedure was followed from the handout supplied by my TA. [Author names if known], (2013) [Experiment Name].

Safety Rules

As you perform your experiment pay special attention to all directions printed in boxes; these are important safety precautions and instructions. **VIOLATING SAFETY RULES AND PRECAUTIONS CAN BE GROUNDS FOR IMMEDIATE DISMISSAL FROM THE LABORATORY AND RESULT IN A SCORE OF ZERO FOR THE EXPERIMENT.**

You do not have to record the safety rules, just follow them.

Reagents and Equipment

The reagents and equipment used in your experiments must be noted and described. These can appear in a list at the beginning of your data and observations section, or can be noted as you use them.

- Note the appearance and concentration of all chemical solutions.

- Record model and serial number of any instruments used.

- Record the sizes of volumetric glassware used.

Procedure Description

Your procedure descriptions should be sufficiently detailed that anyone who reads your report can understand the various steps you took in the execution of it. However, it should not be so detailed that it reads like a step-by-step list of instructions. Knowing what information must be included in it, and what information can be reasonably inferred and therefore left out, is in many ways a matter of experience. As you progress through this course, you will gain this experience and, therefore, an understanding of what procedural steps should be recorded. The following may help you start out in this.

- The methods used to initiate a reaction must be described. For instance, you might say "a Bunsen burner was used to heat the sample of reagent X until it was red-hot." However, you would not have to precede this description with "a Bunsen burner was obtained, its gas turned on and then a sparker was used to light it."

- Quantities of reagents and/or the methods used to measure them out must be recorded or described.

- The procedures for the equipment described in Appendix B can be inferred and, therefore, do not have to be described in your procedure. For instance, you could say that "a 10.00 mL pipette was used to dispense this solution," but since the steps required to use the pipette are described in Appendix B, you would not have to describe how exactly the pipette was used.

Due to the nature of laboratory experiments, there will times when your actions deviate slightly (key word is *slightly*) from the procedure in the manual. For example, you may add a little more of a solution than what is called for in the manual, or a sample may be heated for a longer time period than is indicated. Since these kinds of changes may or may not make a difference in the results, it is important to record exactly what you did rather than what you were supposed to do. This will allow you to properly analyze your data later on should any of your results differ from what you expected.

Data

There are two kinds of data that you will work with in this course: quantitative data and qualitative data.

Quantitative Data

Quantitative, or numerical, data include such things as solution concentrations, volume readings, and length measurements. As part of this course, you are expected to become accustomed to knowing when you should record numerical information in your notebook without being reminded to do so. To help you with this, remember that *the following types of numbers must always be recorded*. Be aware that you will not be explicitly told to record any of these things in the procedure sections of your experiments. Additionally, all numeric data must be recorded to the correct number of significant figures, have units, and be clearly labeled.

- All solution concentrations

- Any number you read from an instrument or from your glassware

- The sizes of volumetric glassware. As a general rule, beakers, Erlenmeyer flasks, and any piece of glassware without an index mark on it (index marks are defined in Appendix B) are not considered "volumetric," but all other pieces of glassware are.

- Any calculation that is performed by a computer program

- The time required for a reaction to finish

  - If this time is less than about 10 seconds, you can approximate the time elapsed or simply say "instantly," or "after a few seconds."

  - If this time takes more than 10 seconds, use a watch/clock to record the actual number of seconds or minutes.

If this list seems daunting, it may help you to simply remember one basic rule: if something has a number associated with it, that number needs to be written down.

Qualitative Data

In contrast to quantitative data, qualitative data largely consist of non-numerical observations such as color, temperature, odor, general appearance, etc. . These types of observations and descriptions must be made before, during, and after you initiate a reaction or add two reagents together. Since it can be difficult to predict which, if any, of these things will change during a reaction, it is important that you describe your reagents as thoroughly as you can before you begin. Once a reaction has been initiated, if the reagents effervesce, form a precipitate, emit smoke, change their color, etc., how quickly and/or vigorously they do so should be noted as well.

The following sample notebook entry depicts an appropriate qualitative data record. It describes the reactions of copper and zinc metal with sulfuric acid.

Sample Notebook Entry

> *Reaction of Solid Metals with Acid (H_2SO_4)*
> *Procedure (used for three different metals)*
> *One piece of copper and another of zinc metal were polished with sand paper and then placed into two different test tubes.*
>
> *The 1 M H_2SO_4 that will be used here is a clear, colorless liquid.*

Here is a list of rules for recording qualitative data and some common errors made in recording procedures and observations. These are points on which you will be graded.

- The methods used to create and/or dilute solutions must be noted.

- The procedure and observations should be written in complete sentences. Any short-hand or abbreviations used must be clearly defined for the reader.

- Do not confuse conclusions with observations. "No reaction took place" is a conclusion, not an observation. "No changes were observed" is an observation, provided you gave a description of what you are working with prior to initiating the reaction.

- When you observe a reaction in an aqueous solution, note all of the following kinds of observations in your book: time, color, transparency, temperature, and the formation of bubbles or a precipitate.
  - "Clear" indicates the solution is transparent, but is not a color; it contrasts with "cloudy."
  - "Cloudy" implies the solution has solid particles in suspension and is also not a color.
  - A solution or suspension that is colored can be either clear or cloudy. If you note a solution is colored, it will therefore also be necessary to note whether it is clear or cloudy.

- As mentioned previously, it is important to always record what you *did* rather than what the instructions in the manual directed you to do.

Late/Non-Submitted Data and Observations

The data and observations portion of your lab report is due in lab at the designated ending time for your section. As for the pre-lab, if it is not submitted on time, a late penalty of 20% will be applied to the entire lab report associated with it for each day it is late. If you forget to turn in your data before you leave lab, it may be submitted to the General Chemistry Office in Fulmer 319A.

Any procedure or observation not signed by your TA before leaving lab will not be graded.

POST-LAB: CALCULATIONS

Many of your labs will require you to perform a series of calculations with your data. When you do this, keep the following in mind:

- All work must be shown.

- Calculations must be legible, labeled, and easy to follow.

- All numbers—not just your final answer—must be labeled and have units.

Data Plots

Some of the experiments that include calculations will involve graphs, in which the data from two different types of measurements will be correlated with each other. For example, consider the height of a plant and its age. (See Figure: Plant Height vs. Age.) If the heights and ages of several plants are plotted on a graph, the points would suggest a trend in which an older plant tended to also be a taller plant. These types of plots, called scatter plots, are used to identify trends in data. A plot should use a full page, have labeled axes with units and with a scale that distributes the points across the full range, and a title.

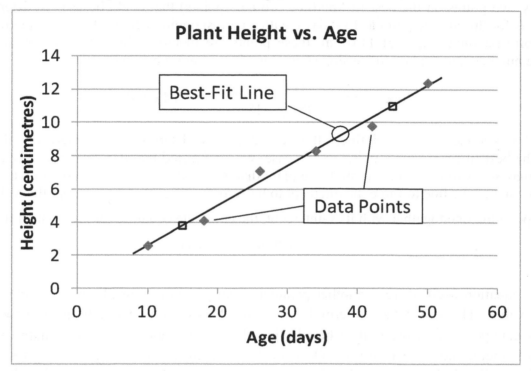

Figure: Plant Height vs. Age. The gray diamonds are data points, the hollow boxes are used to determine the slope of the line of best fit. Note that the best-fit line does not pass through all the data points.

Once a group of data points have been plotted onto a graph, the specific relationship between them can be indicated by drawing a line through them called a best-fit line. These lines will not necessarily pass through every data point, nor the origin (x = 0 and y = 0), but should lie in the middle of all the data points; they are a *best* fit and not a perfect-fit. Although the shapes of these lines can be somewhat complex, in this course we will only use straight, or linear, best-fit lines.

The graphs you will work with in this course will typically be constructed for you by a computer and printed out in lab. They will automatically have most of the features required for full credit, *except best-fit lines drawn through their data points.*

Linear Equations

Once the data have been plotted and a best fit line drawn through them, that line can be used to determine a mathematical expression, or equation, for the parameters under study. The equations for these lines are functions that relate y to x, where a mathematical operation is done to x to give y. In this course, all of your data will exhibit a linear relationship, so the only mathematical function that will be used is the one for a straight line:

$$y = mx + b.$$

The term "b" in this equation is the y-intercept, which is the point where the best-fit line crosses the y-axis at $x = 0$. The term "m" is the slope of the line, which can be determined from two x values and their corresponding y values:

$$\text{slope} = m = \frac{y_2 - y_1}{x_2 - x_1} = \frac{\Delta y}{\Delta x}$$

If we were to determine the equation for the best fit line in the plant height versus age graph, we would first need to identify two points on the best-fit line (not two data points) that could be used to determine its slope. Two possibilities for this are the point at 15.0 days, with a corresponding height of 3.8 cm, and the point at 45.0 days with a corresponding height of 11.0 cm; these points are identified by the hollow boxes in the figure above. If these numbers are applied to the slope equation, that equation becomes:

$$\text{slope} = m = \frac{11.0_{cm} - 3.8_{cm}}{45.0_{days} - 15.0_{days}} = 0.24 \text{ cm/day}$$

Now that the line's slope has been defined, the next step is to determine its y-intercept. This is done by extrapolating the best fit line to the y-axis. In this case, we would find that it crosses the axis at about 0.2 cm. Although this may seem strange, since it implies a plant that is zero days old has already grown a little, it would be improper to "fudge" the line to force the intercept to be zero; we must therefore accept this value as it is.

Putting the slope of the line together with its y-intercept, the complete equation for this best-fit line is:

$$y = (0.24 \text{ cm/day})x + 0.2 \text{ cm}$$

R^2 Value

Aside from the equation itself, there is another parameter that you must consider when working with lines of best fit: the R^2 value. This is a statistical term that measures how close to perfectly linear the relationship of y and x is. If the data points are close to their best-fit line, then R^2 will approach its maximum value of 1. If the data are highly scattered, non-linear, or y is independent of x, then R^2 will be significantly less than 1. In this course, your data will only be considered to be "truly" linear if the R^2 value associated with them is 0.98 or greater.

Unlike the determination of the equation for a best-fit line, the calculation of an R^2 value is a somewhat complicated process. These will therefore be calculated for you by a computer program.

POST-LAB: RESULTS AND DISCUSSION

The last part of each lab report will consist of a results and discussion section. The specific requirements for these will be provided either online or in a handout.

At your instructor's discretion, some or all of your results and discussions will begin with 1-2 paragraphs in which you will summarize the experiment you just performed. This summary should be written so that a reader will understand the following points:

- The experiment's objectives; that is, what were you trying to accomplish?

- A brief description of the methods used in your experiment; i.e., what you did/how you did it. Note that this part should be crafted to read as an overview of your methods, not a step-by-step list of instructions.

- A summary of your results. Specific instructions in the post-lab sections of the various experiments will generally help you with this part by describing what sorts of things you should report here.

In addition to these things, you may also be prompted to describe errors and/or problems encountered, discuss how these errors affected your results, and provide suggestions for what you could have done to mitigate them. For a description of what types of errors can affect an experiment, see the background to the experiment "Laboratory Techniques and Measurements".

Aside from prompting you to describe your results and errors, each experiment may also contain additional topics to cover in the discussion that are specific to the experiment at hand. As you address these topics, be sure to explain your responses to them. Provided you demonstrate that you understand the concepts covered in lab, you can still get points for this section even if you answer a question incorrectly or your results are poor. You may include information from an outside source for this provided this source is properly cited (even if it is your textbook).

One common topic for a discussion is the comparison of two or more calculated and/or measured quantities. This comparison can be between your own value and a 'literature' value, or between multiple values that you obtained. To compare two values, first state the two numbers with their error ranges (see the background to the "Lab Techniques" experiment for a discussion of "error ranges"). Then, state whether or not the two values are significantly different from each other. Finally, provide an explanation of how you determined whether or not the values were significantly different. For the purposes of this course, the two values are significantly different if their error ranges do not overlap in any way. As a general rule, we will use the average value and the standard deviation to determine the error range of a measured value. If another method is used, that method will be indicated/described by the experiment or the source. If no error measurement is given, use +/- 1 in the least significant digit as the error range. For example, if a source lists the density of iron as 7.86 g/mL with no error range, use a range of 7.85 g/mL to 7.87 g/mL.

The paragraphs in which you cover the various points of your results and discussion must be grammatically correct and written in complete sentences. As mentioned in the introduction to this section, they must also be neat and legible.

Late Post-Labs

See your course syllabus for your instructor's policies on late pre-lab assignments.

CITING SOURCES

You will occasionally have to look up information and cite the source, such as a textbook or a journal article, where you obtained this information. The following examples show how to properly cite a reference:

Book

The basic format for a book citation is:

Authors. (year) *Book Title*. Publisher, Publisher's city, state (if known)

Example:

Taiz, Lincoln, and Zeiger, Eduardo. (1998) *Plant Physiology*, 2nd ed. Sinauer Associates, Inc., Sunderland, Massachusetts.

Journal Article

Scientific journals are the primary means by which scientists and other professionals report their findings and discoveries. It will help your academic career immensely to become familiar with them.

A journal article citation is similar to a book citation, except the title of the article precedes the name of the journal itself. Also, instead of the publisher's name and city, the volume and page numbers the article appeared in are noted:

Authors. (year) Article Title. *Journal Name*. Volume Number: page numbers

Example:

Rutherford, E. (1911) The Scattering of α and β Particles by Matter and the Structure of the Atom. *Philosophical Magazine Series 6.* 21: 669-688.

Web Sites

As with journal articles, web site citations include the author of the information on the page and the name of the page itself (which substitutes for the article title). Unlike a book chapter or journal article, it will not always be clear who the author of a web page was or who sponsored the page. Just include what information you do have about the site.

Author. Web Site Owner or Sponsor. *Web Site Name/Title.* Site address (accessed [date you accessed it]).

Examples:

Winter, M. WebElements. *Copper: the essentials.* http://www.webelements.com/copper/ (accessed Sept 14, 2010).

U. S. Department of Health and Human Services, National Institutes of Health. *Selenium in diet.* http://www.nlm.nih.gov/medlineplus/ency/article/002414.htm (accessed Sept 31, 2010).

Quality of Sources

Due to the fact that some sources are more trustworthy than others, the figures provided by different sources vary in their quality. Those of best-quality are from recent primary sources. These are the findings from original research published in a journal that is selective and uses peer review, which is review by other scientists in the field, of the submissions before publication. Secondary sources are those that do not include new research, but that cite the primary sources for the information they present. Lower quality sources are those that just list data without citing the source.

Information is expected to be of higher quality if the organization producing it is respected and generally considered trustworthy. Thus, a value from the National Institute of Standards and Technology (a U.S. Government Institute that does its own research) is better than a value from a textbook, and a value from a textbook is better than an unsubstantiated value from a web site. Keep this in mind if you cannot find a primary source for a value you need.

SAMPLE LAB REPORT

The sample lab report on the following pages has been written according to the guidelines provided in this chapter. It describes an experiment in which the molar mass of a volatile liquid (a liquid with a low boiling point) was determined.

Sample Lab Report

The Molecular Weight of a Volatile Liquid   4/31/2016
Jane Q Student   Chem 105, section 58   TA: Sarah Bowdin

Procedure
The procedure was followed from the General Chemistry Laboratory Manual: Rice et al., Star Publishing, 2015, pages 458-492.

Data and Observations
For this lab, I selected unknown 3. It is a clear liquid that has the consistency of water. It also has a few small black particles that have settled to the bottom of the vial it came in.

For all trials, the liquid was volatilized in an Erlenmeyer flask capped with a piece of foil 5 cm on each side. All masses were measured on a top-loading balance, number 367-80.

	Trial 1	Trial 2
Mass of flask and foil (empty)	76.451 g	76.466 g
Mass of flask, foil, and condensed liquid	77.801 g	77.809 g
Temperature of water bath	97.5°C	97.4°C

Barometric Pressure: 658.01 torr

A cylinder with a total volume of 250 ml was used to determine the total volume of the flask: Its volume was determined to be 139.7 ml

Calculations

	Trial 1	Trial 2
Mass of condensed liquid	76.801 g	77.809 g
	-76.451 g	-76.466 g
	0.350 g	0.343 g

Number of moles using $n = \dfrac{PV}{RT}$

Trial 1:

$$n = \frac{658\,torr}{0.0820575\,\frac{L \cdot atm}{mol \cdot K}} \times \frac{1.00\,atm}{760\,torr} \times \frac{139.7\,ml}{} \times \frac{1.00\,L}{1000\,ml} \times \frac{1}{(273.15+97.5)K} = 3.9767 \times 10^{-3}\,mol$$

Trial 2:

$$n = \frac{658\,torr}{0.0820575\,\frac{L \cdot atm}{mol \cdot K}} \times \frac{1.00\,atm}{760\,torr} \times \frac{139.7\,ml}{} \times \frac{1.00\,L}{1000\,ml} \times \frac{1}{(273.15+97.4)K} = 3.9778 \times 10^{-3}\,mol$$

Calculations (continued)

Molecular Weight (g/mol)

Trial 1: $\dfrac{0.350\,g}{3.9767 \times 10^{-3}\,mol} = 88.013\,g/mol$

Trial 2: $\dfrac{0.343\,g}{3.9778 \times 10^{-3}\,mol} = 86.229\,g/mol$

Average molar mass $= \dfrac{88.013\,g/mol + 86.229\,g/mol}{2} = 87.121\,g/mol$

Standard deviation:

$(88.013\,g/mol - 87.121\,g/mol)^2 + (86.229\,g/mol - 87.121\,g/mol)^2 = 1.591\,g/mol$

$\sqrt{\dfrac{1.591\,g/mol}{1}} = 1.261\,g/mol$

Results and Discussion
Submitted On-Line

In this experiment we determined the molecular mass of an unknown liquid. A volatile liquid was vaporized in a container of known volume, re-condensed, and the mass of the condensed liquid determined. Since the volume, pressure, and temperature of the volatilized liquid was known, it was possible to use the Ideal Gas Law to determine the moles of gas—and therefore moles of re-condensed liquid—present in it. The calculated values for both moles and mass of volatile liquid present were then used to calculate the sample's molecular mass.

As part of this experiment, we performed our procedure with a known liquid: methanol. This has a molar mass of 32.04 g/mol. The molar mass we calculated from our data was 32.67 grams per mole, with a standard deviation of 0.8801 grams/mole. Since the range of this standard deviation around its average, 31.79 g/mol to 33.55 g/mol, encompasses the "true" molar mass of the known, the methods we used here can provide an accurate assessment of a liquid.

The molar mass of unknown number three was determined to be 86.10 g/mol, with a standard deviation of 1.261 grams/mole. This affords a molar mass range from 84.84 g/mol to 87.36 g/mol. As the molar mass of hexane and pentanal both fit within this range, our unknown could be either of these substances.

The flask, foil, and rubber band had significantly more mass after the first trial than after the second trial. It is possible this was due to water that condensed under the foil after the first trial. The mass of this condensed water would have added to the apparent mass of the condensed liquid in the first trial. If the water were still present at the start of the second trial, its mass would have been added to the mass of the empty flask. This would result in a smaller calculated value for the condensed liquid in the second trial, which could account for the discrepancy in the condensed liquid masses between the two trials.

Although hexane and pentanal are both good candidates for the identity of the unknown liquid, I can find no mention of black particles being commonly associated with either substance, as I observed unknown 3 to have. I do recall this unknown's vial was corked with a black rubber stopper. If this stopper was old or the unknown caused it to degrade, it is possible bits of it would have flaked off and fallen into the vial. This would account for the presence of the particles in the unknown.

INORGANIC NOMENCLATURE

INTRODUCTION

At various times in your life, you may have found it difficult to understand a passage in a book or magazine because you were not familiar with the vocabulary used in it. In the field of chemistry, a similar type of confusion can arise because of the nomenclature used for various chemicals. Many chemical compounds have several names depending on the manufacturer, country, and use. For example, consider the compound sodium hydrogen carbonate, which also goes by the name sodium bicarbonate and by the common name baking soda. Although a baker would refer to this as "baking soda," a chemical supply company might refer to by one of the other names.

In order to avoid potential confusion in this and similar situations, a more universal system or "language" was developed for referring to chemical compounds: the International Union of Pure and Applied Chemistry (IUPAC) system. Now that you are a General Chemistry student at the college level, you too are a chemist and need to know how compounds are named.

You will need to memorize the naming rules and polyatomic ions presented in this worksheet exercise in order to be successful in this course. You will be expected to know the names and formulas for all future labs, lectures, quizzes and exams.

BACKGROUND

Although this is a first semester General Chemistry course, it is assumed that you are familiar with the Periodic Table. Specifically, you need to be able to recognize the names and symbols of the elements. You should also know which are the metallic and non-metallic elements and the difference between an atom and an element. Review your textbook or get help from your TA if you are not familiar with the Periodic Table. For convenience, there is a Periodic Table on the back cover of this manual.

Ions and their Charges

Neutral atoms or molecules can gain or lose electrons to become negatively or positively charged. Since electrons have a negative charge, if a neutral atom or molecule gains one or more of them it will become a negatively charged entity, an anion. Conversely, the loss of electrons results in a positively charged chemical species, a cation. Single atoms (elements) that gain or lose an electron are called monatomic ions, and molecules that gain or lose electrons are polyatomic ions.

In these examples, elemental potassium loses an electron to become a potassium cation, and the bromine atom gains an electron to become the bromide anion:

$$K \text{ (potassium atom)} \rightarrow K^+ \text{ (potassium cation)} + e^- \text{ (an electron)}$$

$$Br \text{ (bromine atom)} + e^- \text{ (an electron)} \rightarrow Br^- \text{ (bromide anion)}$$

The charge of a monatomic ion can sometimes be predicted by where the element is located in the Periodic Table. In some cases, all the elements of the same column, or family, have the same charge. For example, all of the elements in the alkali metal family, the column of elements starting with lithium, have a charge of +1. In other cases, the first one or two elements in a column always form ions with only one type of charge, but the rest of the elements in that column do not. Aluminum forms a +3 cation, but most of the other elements in its column can carry any one of a few different charges. The transition metals, those elements in columns 1B through 8B at the center of the Periodic Table, form cations with various charges.

A list of monatomic ion charges for each column of the Periodic Table follows. There are cases where the charges of the monatomic ions may differ from those presented here, but you are unlikely to encounter them in General Chemistry.

Column in the Periodic Table	Family Name	Charge of Monatomic Ions
1A	Alkali Metals	+1
2A	Alkaline Earth Metals	+2
1B – 8B	Transition Metals	varies
6A	Chalcogens	varies
7A	Halogens	-1
8A	Noble Gasses	none

Formulas of Ions

Instead of writing out the full name of an ion or compound, the symbols from the periodic table can be used to write out a chemical formula for those ions/compounds instead. These formulae can be thought of as a shorthand notation that stands in for the full name. For example, the formula "NaCl" can be written instead of "sodium chloride." Conventionally, the symbol for the metallic elements in a formula are written first, followed by the non-metals other than oxygen, and oxygen last.

A system of subscripts and parentheses is used in chemical formulae to provide more information on the makeup and construction of the molecule. Subscripts are used to indicate how many atoms of a particular element are in one molecule of the ion or compound. For instance, the "2" in "H_2O" tells us each water molecule has two hydrogen atoms. A subscript of one is implied and not written.

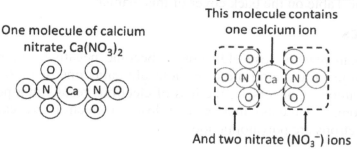

Parentheses are used to indicate a portion of the molecule that can be thought of as an entity by itself. They are used in conjunction with subscripts to indicate how many of these entities there are. For example, consider calcium nitrate, which has the formula $Ca(NO_3)_2$. Note that there are two nitrate ions (NO_3^-, the individual "entity" in this case) for every one calcium ion.

Normally, parentheses are only used this way if more than one "entity" exists in a molecule. The formula for sodium nitrate, $NaNO_3$, which only contains one sodium ion and one nitrate ion per molecule, would not have parentheses around the nitrate

If the atom or molecule is an ion, a superscript will be used to indicate what charge it carries. Cations with a charge of +1, +2, and +3 are given the notation "+", "2+", and "3+" respectively. Anions with a charge of -1, -2, or -3 are given the notation "-", "2-", and "3-" respectively. Note that a charge of one has a + or - sign with no number. Neutral atoms or compounds have a charge of zero and no superscript. Ca^{2+} indicates a calcium ion with a charge of +2; Cl^- indicates a chloride ion with a charge of -1.

It is very important you learn to correctly write chemical formulae. You will lose points throughout this course for dropping or inappropriately using subscripts and superscripts, and not indicating charges.

Cations

Metallic elements almost always lose electrons to form cations. In fact, except for ammonia all of the cations you will encounter in General Chemistry are formed from metallic elements.

Some elements form cations of different charges. The charges of these cations are indicated with a Roman numeral in parentheses after the element symbol. For example, copper can have a +1 charge, Cu(I), or a +2 charge, Cu(II). You will need to recognize the elements that can have cations of different charges and memorize the cations that exist with only a single charge and therefore do not require a Roman numeral. Examples of both situations are given below.

Cations with a +1 Charge

Group 1A (Alkali metals) have a +1 charge (Li^+, Na^+, K^+, Rb^+, Cs^+)

H^+	Proton or Hydrogen
Cu^+	Copper(I)
Ag^+	Silver*
NH_4^+	Ammonium (This is the only common polyatomic cation.)
Hg_2^{2+}	Mercury(I) (This is a diatomic cation of two Hg^+ ions; it is not common.)

Cations with a +2 Charge

Group 2A (Alkaline Earth metals) have a +2 charge (Be^{2+}, Mg^{2+}, Ca^{2+}, Sr^{2+}, Ba^{2+}).

Zn^{2+}	Zinc*	Cd^{2+}	Cadmium*
Cr^{2+}	Chromium(II)	Pb^{2+}	Lead(II)
Ni^{2+}	Nickel(II)	Co^{2+}	Cobalt(II)
Cu^{2+}	Copper(II)	Sn^{2+}	Tin(II)
Fe^{2+}	Iron(II)	Pt^{2+}	Platinum(II)

Cations with a +3 Charge

Al^{3+}	Aluminum	Cr^{3+}	Chromium(III)
Co^{3+}	Cobalt(III)	Fe^{3+}	Iron(III)

Cations with a +4 Charge

Pb^{4+}	Lead(IV)	Sn^{4+}	Tin(IV)

*Silver, zinc, and cadmium only carry charges of +1, +2, and +2 respectively, so no numeral is needed.

Cation Nomenclature

With the exception of ammonium, cations are straightforward to name because they keep the same name as the element. In order to avoid confusing an element with its corresponding cation, the word "ion" is often stated after the element name if it is in ionic form. If the element can have more than one charge, the number is stated after the element name. The "plus" to indicate a positive charge is usually dropped from the spoken name, but can be added for clarification. When writing out the name, the charge is indicated by Roman numerals in parenthesis after the element name, as indicated in the table.

Na^+ is both written and read as "sodium ion"; Cu^{2+} is written as "copper(II) ion" or just "copper(II)", and read "copper two."

Anions

Unlike cations, many anions are polyatomic. Most of these ions consist of one or more elements with oxygen. You will need to memorize the following list of polyatomic anions, including their names, formulas, and charges.

As you look over this list, note the subtle differences in some of the names and formulae. For example, the close similarity of the name and formula for nitrate (NO_3^-) and nitrite (NO_2^-). Be careful you don't confuse these similar-sounding ions with each other.

Anions with a −1 Charge

Group 7A (Halogens) have a −1 charge (F^-, Cl^-, Br^-, I^-) and are named with "-ide", chloride, fluoride, bromide and iodide.

OH^-	Hydroxide	NO_2^-	Nitrite
ClO^-	Hypochlorite	NO_3^-	Nitrate
ClO_2^-	Chlorite	CN^-	Cyanide
ClO_3^-	Chlorate	OCN^-	Cyanate
ClO_4^-	Perchlorate	SCN^-	Thiocyanate
MnO_4^-	Permanganate	$H_2PO_4^-$	Dihydrogen phosphate
HSO_4^-	Hydrogen sulfate	HCO_3^-	Hydrogen carbonate or bicarbonate*
CH_3COO^- (or $C_2H_3O_2^-$)	Acetate		

You also must know the Br and I containing ions, which are analogous to the polyatomic Cl ions. The names can be found by replacing "chlor" with either "brom" or "iod". For example, BrO^- is hypo*brom*ite and IO_4^- is per*iod*ate.

*The proper name for this ion is hydrogen carbonate, though it is more commonly referred by the older name bicarbonate. It is nearly always referred to as bicarbonate on food and drink packaging.

Anions with a −2 Charge

Group 6A (Chalcogens) have a −2 charge (O^{2-}, S^{2-}, Se^{2-}, Te^{2-}) and are named oxide, sulfide, selenide and telluride.

SO_3^{2-}	Sulfite	$C_2O_4^{2-}$	Oxalate
SO_4^{2-}	Sulfate	CrO_4^{2-}	Chromate
$S_2O_3^{2-}$	Thiosulfate	$Cr_2O_7^{2-}$	Dichromate
CO_3^{2-}	Carbonate		
HPO_4^{2-}	Hydrogen phosphate (monohydrogen phosphate)		

Anions with a -3 Charge

Nitrogen and phosphorus form –3 monatomic ions (N^{3-}, and P^{3-}) that are named nitride and phosphide.

PO_4^{3-} Phosphate

Anion Nomenclature

Notice that all the anion names given in the preceding table end in –ide, –ite, or –ate. These suffixes are assigned according to a certain pattern. If you understand the pattern, you can more easily determine the formula of an anion from its name and vice-versa.

The –ide suffix replaces the last three letters of the element name for monatomic anions. It is also used for polyatomic anions that do not contain oxygen. For example, chloride and cyanide. An exception to this rule is thiocyanate.

The –ate and –ite suffixes, in combination with the prefixes hypo- and per- are used for polyatomic anions that contain oxygen. These suffixes and prefixes are assigned to the root name of an anion based on how many oxygen atoms that ion has. The anion species with the fewest number of oxygen atoms has the prefix hypo- and suffix –ite. Add an oxygen, and the name loses the hypo- prefix; another oxygen and the suffix changes to –ate; the prefix per- is added for the addition of yet another oxygen. Examples of these are found in your list of anions.

Anion Prefix and Suffix Use

Anion does not contain oxygen: – ide

Polyatomic anion with oxygen:

- fewest number of oxygens: hypo– and –ite

- one more oxygens: –ite

- two more oxygens: –ate

- greatest number of oxygens: per– and –ate

Naming Compounds

Compounds are combinations of more than one element. Although they may be composed of charged ions, their combined, net charge will be neutral. Those you will most often encounter in this course can be divided into two groups: ionic compounds that are composed of a cation and an anion, and molecular compounds that consist of atoms joined together that are not ions. Ionic compounds can be further divided into two sub-groups: those in which the cation is a metal, which are also called salts, and those in which the cation is hydrogen, which are acids.

Formulas are a convenient shorthand way to write an ion or compound, but it is important to know the full names in order to talk about the compound. For example, CsO could be read "C. S. O.", which sounds like the very different compound CSO. This type of miscommunication is even more likely if parentheses, superscripts, and/or subscripts are included in the formula.

Ionic Compounds

When naming an ionic compound, the cation is named first, followed by the anion. This applies to both monatomic and polyatomic ions. Thus, in order to name an ionic compound from its formula, simply name the cation and then the anion. If the metal cation can have more than one charge, then the name must include the Roman numeral designation.

Some examples are: NaCl   is sodium chloride.

                   $Ca(NO_3)_2$ is calcium nitrate.

                   $FeCl_2$ is iron(II) chloride.

Determining a cation charge from a formula

If the compound you are naming contains a metal ion that can have more than one charge but you don't know what its charge is, do the following to determine it. We will use $Cu(NO_3)_2$ and $Fe_2(SO_4)_3$ as examples.

1. First, identify the charge on the anions associated with the cation. According to the anion table given above, nitrate (NO_3^-) has a charge of -1 and sulfate (SO_4^{2-}) a charge of -2.

2. Calculate what the sum of the charges on the anions are. There are two nitrates in each formula of $Cu(NO_3)_2$, so the sum of their charges is -2; there are three sulfates in each formula of $Fe_2(SO_4)_3$, so the sum of their charges is -6.

3. Determine what the charges contributed by the cations are. Since both of these salts carry a net charge of zero, the total positive charge given by the copper ion in each formula of $Cu(NO_3)_2$ must be +2; the total charge given by the irons in $Fe_2(SO_4)_3$ must be +6.

4. Finally, calculate the charge on each individual metal ion by dividing their total charge by the number of atoms of them in each formula unit. There is only one copper ion in each formula unit of $Cu(NO_3)_2$, so the charge on each copper must be +2. There are two irons in each formula of $Fe_2(SO_4)_3$, so the charge on each must be +3.

In summary, the copper in $Cu(NO_3)_2$ is Cu (II) (or Cu^{2+}), and the iron in $Fe_2(SO_4)_3$ is Fe (III) (Fe^{3+}).

Note that you will only have to make this determination if the metal ion can have more than one different charge. Ions such as K^+ and Ca^{2+} will only be found with one type of charge.

Determining a formula from a name

Writing a formula for an ionic compound from the name requires the charges of the ions to be known. For metal ions such as Cu (II) and Fe (III), this is fairly easy because the charge is built into the name. For other cations, you will have to learn to determine their charge from their position on the periodic table. For anions, you will have to memorize them.

Once you know what the charges on all the species in an ionic compound are, you then have to determine how many of them there will be in each formula unit. Keep one basic rule in mind when doing this: the net charge on all ionic compounds is zero. Thus the sum of the charge(s) on the cation(s) and the sum of the charge(s) on the anion(s) must be equal and opposite. The following examples will illustrate this point.

Sodium Chloride

Sodium is an alkaline metal so its charge must be +1. Chloride is a halide, so its charge must be -1. Since the charge of a single sodium ion, +1, added to a charge of a single chloride ion, -1, affords a net charge of zero, there must be only one sodium ion and one chloride ion in each formula unit of sodium chloride. The formula of sodium chloride is therefore NaCl.

Calcium chloride

Calcium is an alkaline earth metal so its charge must be +2. Chloride is a halide, so its charge must be -1. In order for the net charge of the molecule to equal zero, there must be two chlorides for every one calcium. The formula of calcium chloride is therefore $CaCl_2$.

Cobalt (III) sulfate

We know from the Roman Numeral in the name that cobalt has a charge of +3 and we know from the anion table sulfate has a charge of -2. The question now becomes what the smallest formula subscripts are that will give us a net charge of zero. For these more complex compounds, there is a handy shortcut you can use to determine how many cations and anions there should be: the charge of each cation becomes the subscript for the anion, and the charge of each anion becomes the subscript for the cation:

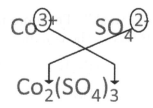

The formula of cobalt (III) sulfate is therefore $Co_2(SO_4)_3$.

Molecular Compounds

Molecular compounds are typically formed from two non-metal elements. Conventionally, the element further to the left, or lower on the periodic table is named first. The second element takes the –ide suffix. A system of prefixes is used to designate the number of atoms of an element that are present in the molecule.

Prefix	Number of Atoms	Example
di–	2	NO_2 is written nitrogen dioxide.
tri–	3	BH_3 is written boron trihydride.
tetra–	4	N_2O_4 is written dinitrogen tetroxide.*
penta–	5	PCl_5 is written phosphorus pentachloride.
hexa–	6	SF_6 is written sulfur hexafluoride.

*Note that the "a" at the end of tetra was dropped because it was followed by a vowel in this case.

Note that some molecular compounds have the same formula as the anions described previously, but are not anions. For example, NO_2^- is nitrite, but NO_2 is nitrogen dioxide. Check the charge when naming these.

Acids and Bases

Acids and bases are specific classes of ionic compounds. They have unique properties in aqueous solutions because of the way the dissociated ions interact with water. You will learn more about the chemistry of acids and bases later, but for now you need to be able to recognize them and their names.

ACIDS

Acids are ionic compounds where the cation is a proton(s). They are named by taking the anion and modifying it as follows.

Anion Suffix	Acid Prefix and Suffix	Example
–ide	Hydro_____ic acid	Chloride (Cl^-) becomes Hydrochloric Acid (HCl)
–ite	–ous acid	Hypochlorite (ClO^-) becomes Hypochlorous Acid (HClO)
–ate	–ic acid	Chlorate (ClO_3^-) becomes Chloric Acid ($HClO_3$)

Hydro Bromous

There a few exceptions to these rules that you will have to know. H_2S is hydrosulf<u>ur</u>ic acid, not "hydrosulfic acid," H_2SO_4 is sulf<u>ur</u>ic acid, not "sulfic acid," and H_3PO_4 is phosph<u>or</u>ic acid, not "phosphic acid."

As for metal salts, the sum of the charges in an acid must equal zero. Since protons always have a charge of +1, the number of them in an acid will therefore be equal to the anion's charge. For example, the carbonate anion has a –2 charge, so two protons are needed to make carbonic acid (the suffix –ic is used because carbonate ends in –ate). The formula for carbonic acid is H_2CO_3.

Acids are generally categorized as "strong" or "weak". For more information on the difference between these, see the experiment "Properties of Acids and Bases." The common strong acids are:

HCl	Hydrochloric acid	HNO_3	Nitric acid
HBr	Hydrobromic acid	H_2SO_4	Sulfuric acid
HI	Hydroiodic acid	$HClO_4$	Perchloric acid

For now, suffice it to say any acid that is not strong is considered weak.

BASES

Bases are a class of ionic compounds that have hydroxide as the anion. The names of most bases follow the normal rules for naming ionic compounds. The one exception you will need to know for General Chemistry is ammonia, NH_3. The common strong bases are those formed from the alkali metals. One of the more common bases, perhaps the single most common, is sodium hydroxide, NaOH.

Flowchart for Naming Inorganic Compounds

You may find the following flowchart useful for determining which naming rules to use when writing a compound name from a formula.

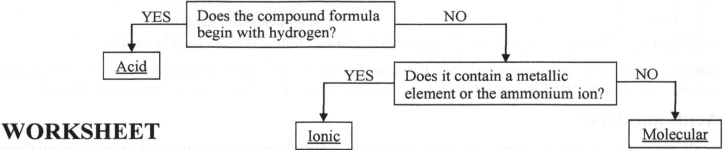

WORKSHEET

You will be handed a worksheet to do during the laboratory period. You are to write the questions and answers in your laboratory notebook.

The report must be handed in at the end of this laboratory period.

STOICHIOMETRY AND CHEMICAL ANALYSIS

INTRODUCTION

All chemical reactions can be expressed as balanced equations that depict the form of the "starting compounds," called reagents, and the "final compounds," called products. Aside from telling you what types of reactions take place, these equations also indicate how much product will be made from a specific amount of reactants. Hence, they obey the principle of conservation of mass: matter is neither created nor destroyed; it is only altered in its form.

The practice of using balanced chemical equations to predict what quantity of product will result from a given quantity of reagents is stoichiometry. Stoichiometry is one of the fundamental principles of chemistry and will be used extensively in Chemistry 105. You will need to be proficient at stoichiometry calculations in order to be successful in this as well as the subsequent 106 course.

In lab, units such as mass and volume are typically used to measure the amounts of reactants used and product made. However, in order to predict how much product will be made from a given quantity of reagents, or determine what quantity of reagents is required to produce a desired quantity of product, it is necessary to know how many molecules of these are involved, rather than the masses or volumes. More commonly, though, these numbers of molecules will be expressed as a number of moles, with one mole equal to 6.022×10^{23} molecules. By analogy, a quantity of eggs is often expressed as a number of dozens, with one dozen equal to 12 eggs. The molar mass of a compound can be used to convert the number of moles of it present into a mass, and vice-versa.

In this worksheet exercise you will practice balancing chemical equations and applying stoichiometry. You will also practice working with units, including converting values from one unit to another. If you are unsure of how to set up and perform these problems, please see your TA or course instructor for help.

WORKSHEET

The worksheet will be distributed in the laboratory and is due at the end of the laboratory period. There are no post-lab questions. The questions on the worksheet are to be written and answered in your laboratory notebook during the lab period and turned in at the end of the lab.

$$NaCl \times \frac{1.5 \text{ moles } Ba(NO_3)_2}{}$$

LABORATORY TECHNIQUES AND MEASUREMENTS

INTRODUCTION

The foundation of all well-executed scientific experiments is the application of good technique when in the laboratory. This is to say that a scientist who conducts an experiment must be familiar with, and be able to properly use, all of their instruments and glassware. Poor laboratory technique could, for example, lead you to determine that the density of air is greater than that of water. Although this is clearly not true, it is entirely possible that a set of poorly taken measurements would say it is.

Aside from being familiar with the operation of a piece of equipment, an experimenter must also understand its limitations. By properly understanding these limitations, it is possible to know what exactly the results from an experiment can, and cannot, tell you. This will enable you to draw the proper conclusions from your experiments and avoid any unwarranted conclusions. To continue the water/air example, although a certain set of instruments might enable you to (correctly) conclude that water is more dense than air, those same instruments might not be accurate enough to say whether the water is more or less dense than a sample of fruit juice. If you were to use them to evaluate the densities of water and juice anyway, these accuracy limitations would preclude the validation of your conclusions.

In this experiment you will evaluate the precision of several pieces of glassware and instruments. You will then use this information to determine the density of a solution you will prepare. As part of this, you will measure its density several times, average your results, and perform a kind of statistical analysis on them. These same statistical techniques will be employed in several other experiments you will perform in this course.

BACKGROUND

Qualitative and Quantitative Analysis

Analyses can be classified into two categories: qualitative and quantitative. The aim of <u>qualitative</u> analysis is to determine what something is, and typically involves data in the form of words (green, soft, shiny, liquid, round, etc.), pictures, or objects. <u>Quantitative</u> analyses, by contrast, are performed to tell how much of something there is; consequently, they involve data in the form of numbers.

Often, the complete analysis of a system will involve both types of analytical techniques. A qualitative analysis will be performed to determine what something is, then a quantitative analysis to determine how much of it is present. For instance, consider a lake that is believed to be contaminated with an unknown substance. To fully understand the extent of the contamination, two things would have to happen: the contaminant would have to be identified and the amount present quantified.

In this experiment, most of your data will be quantitative in nature as they* will consist of mass and volume measurements. However, you will also be required to make qualitative observations about the objects and solutions you will study.

*If it seems strange to you to refer to data as "they," you should know that "data" is, in fact, a plural word.

Significant Figures

Whenever you record numerical data, the precision of your measurement is conveyed by the number of digits you use to record it. These digits are referred to as the significant figures (or "sig figs") of that number. Significant figures include all digits *except*: (1) all zeros to the left of the first non-zero digit and (2) all zeros to the right of the last non-zero digit in numbers that do not have a decimal point. For example, consider the

$$N_A = 6.022 \times 10^{23} \frac{atoms}{mol}$$

Avogadro's #

$$M = \frac{\# \text{ of g in thing}}{1 \text{ mol thing}}$$

numbers 74900 and 0.0130. Although both of these numbers consist of a total of five digits, only three of the five are considered significant:

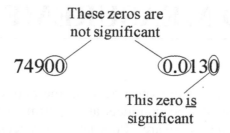

To illustrate the relationship between significant figures and precision, let's assume that the numbers in the above example are length measurements recorded in meters. In this case, a figure of "0.0130 meters" means that the number was measured to the nearest ten-thousandth (or 0.0001 m) of a meter. If the number was reported as "0.013 meters" instead, it would be implied that the measurement was only taken to the nearest thousandth (0.001) of a meter. Because one-thousandth of a meter is a greater (larger) length than one-ten-thousandth, the latter version of the measurement, 0.013 meters, is less precise than 0.0130 meters. Thus, it is desirable to always record your measurements with the greatest number of significant figures your instruments allow.

Since the "normal" way of writing a number can make it unclear how many significant figures it has, it is often preferable to report numbers in scientific notation instead. In this system, numbers are written as a coefficient multiplied by a power of ten. The number 74900 in the above example would be written as $7.49 \cdot 10^4$ in scientific notation; 0.0130 would be written as $1.30 \cdot 10^{-2}$. In this system, all of the digits in the coefficient are significant figures.

Data Error and Variability

Experimenter Error

All measurements are subject to various kinds of errors. One type of these is due to the fact that, no matter how much care one may invest in his or her work, mistakes happen. Mistakes that are caused by the person conducting the experiment are called, appropriately, experimenter errors. Fortunately, with practice these can be avoided and, if they happen, identified and corrected. As a general rule, it is desirable to correct any mistakes should they occur. However, if the mistake is only acknowledged when it is too late to correct it, its consequences on the outcome of the experiment must be considered. Since it is not always clear when a mistake is made while in lab, it is important to have a record of everything you do in your laboratory notebook.

If you make any experimenter errors in lab you will be asked to discuss the effect they may have had on your results in your write-up for the experiment. However, *you will not receive credit for an error analysis that only includes experimenter error*. You must also account for other types of error, such as those described below.

Data Variability

A second type of error manifests itself as variation in the data collected (note that, unlike experimenter errors, here the term "error" is not synonymous with "mistake"). For measurements that do not involve many significant figures in the measured value, it is possible to measure something several times and get the same result each time. However, for work that involves measurements with a large number of significant figures, it is readily possible to take several different measurements of the same object and obtain slightly different answers. For instance, if you were to measure the length of a wooden rod several times with a ruler marked only in centimeters and made no effort to interpolate between the marks, you may find it measures 47 centimeters each time you take the measurement. However, because of tiny variations in the wood at the rod's ends, if you were to measure the length of that same rod five times with an instrument that allows readings to 0.01 cm, that instrument might return lengths of 47.01 cm, 46.98 cm, 47.02 cm, 46.97 cm, and 47.02 cm. There are countless other examples of situations where these types of errors can insert themselves into an experiment. Just a few include:

- The reading on a thermometer fluctuates slightly when a temperature is taken.

- A single plant in a botanical study receives slightly more light than others in that same study

- A few drops of liquid cling to the inside of a piece of glassware instead of being dispensed

Any of these situations can cause variability in experimental data, with corresponding variability in any calculations performed with those data. Because of this, it is considered poor practice to draw conclusions from a single observation; a single data point might not reflect the "true" nature of the system under study, and cannot indicate any variation that occurs when the measurement is repeated. Instead, whenever an experiment is conducted, several trials of it will be performed and several sets of data collected from those trials.

Unfortunately, having multiple data points presents another problem: they make it difficult to conclusively summarize the nature of the system under study; e.g., is our wooden rod 47.01 cm long or 46.98 cm? The figures you collect could be averaged into a single figure, but this average would not say anything about the variability in the numbers used to calculate it. However, it is important to account for this because, as we will see, the degree to which your figures vary from each other has implications for the reliability of your results. What we would need in order to report the variation in the data is a set of numbers that demonstrate if the data are tightly clustered around their average, or if they are widely spaced around it. To get these numbers, we turn to statistics.

Statistics

Statistics is a branch of mathematics that is concerned with the analysis and interpretation of numerical data. Like chemistry, it is a broad topic that encompasses a variety of sub-topics and techniques. Although many of its concepts are beyond the scope of this course, there is one that you will become familiar with: the standard deviation.

Calculation of the Standard Deviation

The standard deviation of a set of numbers is, roughly speaking, a measurement of how much those numbers vary from their average. Thus, data that vary widely from their average would have a higher standard deviation than data that cluster tightly around their average. To calculate the standard deviation of a group of numbers, follow these steps:

1. First, calculate the mean (i.e., the average) of the numbers you are analyzing. In the case of the rod measurements mentioned above, their average is 47.00 cm.

2. Next, take one of the numbers used to calculate the mean, subtract the mean from it, and square the resultant number:

$$([value] - [mean])^2$$

If we did this with the first rod measurement, this would return a value of 0.0001 cm^2. This same operation is then done on all remaining numbers.

3. Add together (or sum) all of the numbers that were calculated in the previous step. For the rod, this would afford a value of 0.0022 cm^2.

4. Take the number of figures you have minus one and divide your answer to the previous step by this number. Since there are five figures in our rod example, we would divide 0.0022 cm^2 by 4.

5. Take the square root of the previous step. In our example, this would return 0.02345 cm

The equation that summarizes what you just did is:

$$\text{Standard Deviation} = \sqrt{\frac{\Sigma(X_i - M)^2}{N-1}}$$

Where M is the average of all the numbers used, X_i is the value of any given number, Σ is a mathematical symbol that means "add them all together," and N is the number of values you are analyzing.

This final number calculated in the last step, 0.02345 cm, is the standard deviation of the five rod length measurements. Note that it is only 0.05% of the average. For comparison, consider what would happen if we were to perform the same calculations on rods that measured 42.09 cm, 53.39 cm, 45.52 cm, 43.91 cm, and 50.09 cm in length. The average of these numbers is also 47.00 cm, but their standard deviation is 4.643 cm, or nearly 10% of their average (see Figure 1.1). Also note how dissimilar these five measurements are in comparison to the measurements taken on the first rod.

If you have taken a statistics course, you have likely seen a similar version of this equation in which the product of the third step is divided by the total number of figures, rather than this number minus 1. This alternate form of the equation is used to calculate the standard deviation of an entire population of data, as opposed to a sample of it. However, small sets of data such as the ones you will collect are more properly treated as samples rather than whole populations.

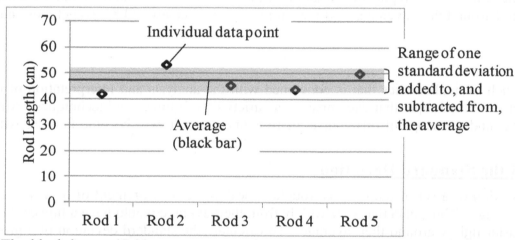

Figure 1.1. The black bar at 47.00 cm represents the average of 42.09 cm, 53.39 cm, 45.52 cm, 43.91 cm, and 50.09 cm. The gray shaded area around the bar encompasses the region one standard deviation above and one standard deviation below the average.

Application of the Standard Deviation

In this course, if you are asked to calculate a number for a system under study (e.g., determine how long or dense an object is), you must consider that your answer could be anything in the range the standard deviation lies around the average. Since the measurements of our first rod had an average of 47.00 cm and a standard deviation of 0.02345, its length would be reported as being between 46.98 cm and 47.02 cm. You could not truthfully be any more precise than that.

The range of plus and minus one standard deviation about a number will be used in this course to compare two numbers; that is, to say whether the two numbers are the same, or if they are significantly different from each other. If you are comparing a number that has a standard deviation associated with it to one that does not, then the comparison is a matter of whether or not the second number falls inside the range of the first. For example, let's say you are given the task of identifying an unknown liquid. To this end, you collect several sets of data that allow you to calculate the density of the liquid several times. This analysis tells you the liquid's density is 0.790 g/mL with a standard deviation of 0.020 g/mL; you therefore conclude that its density is somewhere between 0.770 g/mL and 0.810 g/mL. Since the density of water, 0.998 g/mL, falls outside this range, you can conclude that the substance is not water.

A comparison of two numbers that both have standard deviation ranges is somewhat similar. For the purposes of this course, if the standard deviation ranges around two numbers overlap, you may conclude there is no significant difference between these numbers. For instance, consider another group of rods with an average length of 47.03 cm and a standard deviation of 0.03 cm. Since the range of this standard deviation around its average is 47.00 cm to 47.06 cm, a range which overlaps with that of the rods in the earlier group that had an average length of 47.00 cm and a standard deviation of 0.02 cm, this group of rods would not be considered to have a different length than the rods in the earlier group.

It is worth mentioning that, in professional work, there are more advanced statistical techniques that are often used in lieu of the standard deviation to account for the variability in data sets. When you take a statistics course, you will learn some of these techniques and how to apply them. However, in this course it will be sufficient to use the standard deviation in the manner described.

Data Quality: Precision

Precision in Data Sets versus Data Points

Up until now, we have used the term "precision" to refer to the number of significant figures in numerical data. However, it can also be used to describe the degree to which data points vary from their average, which, as mentioned, is reflected in the size of their standard deviation. In the case of the wooden rod, the measurements of the first rod would be considered relatively precise; their standard deviation was small and the largest measurement was no more than 0.05 cm larger than the smallest. Naturally, the smaller the standard deviation, the more precise the data set.

When describing the quality of data, it is important to consider that data's "precision" in both senses of the word; that is, in both a "significant figures" sense as well as a "standard deviation" sense. This is because how precise a data set is by the former measure affects how precise it is in the other. In the above example of the rod's measurements, we mentioned that if the rod's length were only measured to the ones place it might be possible to measure its length several times and observe the same length each time. Since these numbers would afford a standard deviation of zero, it may seem that the precision of these data is superior to that from the measurements taken to the hundredths place. However, this is not the case. Because the number "47 cm" is only recorded to the ones place, it provides no information as to what the true length of the rod, and any variation in that length, is to the nearest 0.01 cm or even the nearest 0.1 cm. In other words, it effectively tells us that the rod's length could be anything between 46.5 cm and 47.4 cm. Therefore, the measurements taken to the ones places are actually "sloppier" than those taken to the hundredths despite their smaller standard deviation. Thus, it is desirable to always record your data to a higher number of significant figures even if this results in a larger standard deviation.

Unless stated otherwise, we will use the term "precision" to refer to the variation in data for the remainder of this manual. This is simply to avoid potential confusion; both are equally valid uses of the term.

Precision Requirements

Now that we know a way to describe/report the variation in the data, how much should be tolerated? Put another way, how precise do the data need to be? The answer to this is, unfortunately, not simple because it depends upon the requirements of the experiment at hand. Going back to the example in which the density of an unknown liquid was calculated, although a calculated density of 0.770 g/mL to 0.810 g/mL enabled you to determine the liquid was not water, you could not use this information to distinguish between ethanol and propanol, which have densities of 0.789 g/mL and 0.803 g/mL respectively. You could therefore conclude that the unknown is either ethanol or propanol but not water. If you had to distinguish between these, your precision would first have to improve.

Data Quality: Accuracy

Precision is only one measure of the overall quality of a data set. Another is that set's accuracy, which is a measure of how close the figures in it are to their "true" value. To illustrate this, let's say the procedure used to determine the density of an unknown liquid above was performed on water. If the results indicated that the water has a density of 0.998 g/mL at room temperature, which is in fact equal to its known density, then than we could consider the result to be highly accurate.

Unfortunately, aside from the more obvious sources of error mentioned above, it is possible for an experimental procedure to contain some hidden flaw that compromises the accuracy of the results derived from it. If this were the case, it would be possible for these results to be inaccurate even if the researcher who utilized the procedure was careful and did not make any experimenter mistakes. To continue the density of water example, let's assume that, over the course of five trials, the measurements taken on the water reveal its density to be 0.89 g/mL, 0.90 g/mL, 0.88 g/mL, 0.90 g/mL and 0.87 g/mL. These numbers are reasonably precise; they are all close to their average of 0.89 g/mL and have a standard deviation of 0.012 g/mL. However, since the actual density of water is 0.998 g/mL, they are inaccurate despite being precise.

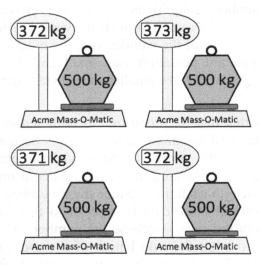

Figure 1.2: Accuracy versus precision. The four readings given by these four different scales are fairly precise: their standard deviation is 0.816 kg, compared to an average reading of 372 kg. However, since the weights placed on the scales are 500 kg, the readings are inaccurate despite this precision.

Use of a Positive Control

Because of the potential for these kinds of accuracy errors, it is always necessary to perform your experiments and measurements on a system or object for which you already know the properties: a positive control. Only after the methods used in your experiment have been validated in this way can they be used to analyze a system with unknown properties. In the case of the water experiment, the technique used would not be considered valid unless the true density of water fell within the results' standard deviation range.

Experimental Overview

The kinds of analyses you will perform in this experiment all share one common theme: they depend upon the calculation of the density of a substance. Therefore, before we cover what your experimental objectives are, we will cover the basic principles of density.

Density

The density of an object or substance is its mass per unit volume (or, colloquially, how much something weighs for its size). Two measurements of a substance must be taken to determine its density: the mass of a particular sample of the substance and the volume of the same sample. To calculate density, the former is divided by the latter. Typical density units are g/mL or g/cm^3.

It is common for the density of a substance to vary with its temperature. For example, the density of liquid water is 1.0000 g/mL at 4.0°C, but at 20.0°C it is 0.99823 g/mL. You may note from this example that the mass of a fixed *volume* of water decreases as its temperature increases. Conversely, if the temperature of a fixed *mass* of water were to increase, the volume of that sample would also increase. This is sometimes observed in the expansion of water, oil, and metal rods as they "warm up."

Experimental Objectives

The primary objective of this experiment is to examine the relationship between the concentration of a solution and its density. To accomplish this, you will have to make a solution of known concentration and measure the density of it. Meanwhile, your classmates will do the same, but they will make their own solutions to a different concentration than you do. Ultimately, you will pool your own data with theirs to create a data plot similar to the "Plant Height vs. Age" plot in the Laboratory Report Guidelines chapter. This will enable you to address the following question: is there a correlation between the density of a solution and its concentration?

Overview of the solution density portion of this experiment

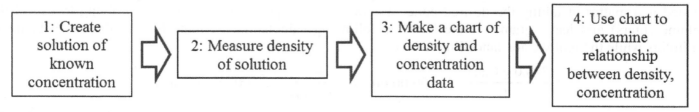

For reasons we have covered elsewhere in this chapter, the measurements you will take to determine the density of your solution will be susceptible to errors that may compromise their precision and/or accuracy. Therefore, it will be necessary to take multiple measurements to evaluate their precision, and also to calculate the density of a known substance to evaluate the accuracy of your technique. The substance you will use for the latter is deionized water (DI water).

Preparation of a Stock Solution

Part of your procedure will require you to prepare a stock solution of calcium chloride in a volumetric flask. The procedure for this is described in Appendix B.

Equipment and Techniques

The principal goal of this lab is to introduce you to some of the more commonly used types of glassware and techniques in General Chemistry. You will be expected to know how to properly use this glassware and perform these techniques for all subsequent General Chemistry labs. Equipment descriptions are provided in Appendix A. Common techniques, including equipment usage, are described in Appendix B. Take the time to review the following pieces of equipment in Appendix A, and the techniques in Appendix B. This will save you time in the lab.

Cleanliness	Top Loading Balance	Volumetric Pipette
Rinsing Glassware	Weigh by Difference	Standard Solutions
Reading a Meniscus	Graduated Cylinder	

Calculations

Density

As mentioned previously, the density of an object or substance can be calculated by dividing its mass by its volume. If you do this for an object with a mass of 5.46 grams and a volume of 2.46 mL, you will find that this object has a density of 2.22 g/mL.

Calculating a Desired Solution Concentration

Since the calcium chloride solution you will make needs to be made to a precise concentration, you will make it in a volumetric flask. This will require you to calculate the amount of calcium chloride needed for the size of your flask. Furthermore, this calculation will be somewhat complicated by the fact you will be given calcium chloride dihydrate, $CaCl_2 \cdot 2H_2O$, rather than anhydrous calcium chloride, $CaCl_2$, to make the solution. The "$2H_2O$" portion of the former's formula refers to its waters of hydration. As we will see, it will be necessary to account for these when calculating the mass of a desired portion of calcium chloride.

There are a few ways to calculate the quantity of $CaCl_2 \cdot 2H_2O$ required to make a solution of a given concentration. One is to begin by calculating the amount of $CaCl_2$ that will be needed, then factoring in the mass of the waters of hydration later. For example, let's say you are provided with a 200.00 mL flask and asked to make a solution with a concentration of 300.0 grams $CaCl_2$ per liter. Determining the amount of $CaCl_2$ needed is a matter of taking the desired concentration in grams per liter (g/L) and multiplying to cancel the volume (liters) and leave grams. Note how the following calculation accounts for the flask size being in milliliters while the unit we are cancelling is liters:

$$\frac{300.0 \text{ g } CaCl_2}{L} \text{ X } 200.00 \text{ mL X } \frac{L}{1000 \text{ mL}} = 60.00 \text{ grams } CaCl_2$$

Our 300.0 g/L solution can therefore be made by dissolving 60.00 grams of $CaCl_2$ into a final volume of 200.00 mL. As we mentioned previously, however, your solution will be made from $CaCl_2 \cdot 2H_2O$, not $CaCl_2$. Since the former's waters of hydration will affect the mass of chemical measured out, they must be factored into our calculation of the mass of chemical needed to make the solution.

The waters of hydration can be accounted for in much the same way a balanced chemical equation and the molar masses of the reactants and products in that equation can be used to predict the mass of product made from a mass of reactant. First, it is necessary to know how many moles of $CaCl_2$ are in 60.00 grams of this compound. The molar mass of $CaCl_2$ is 110.98 g/mol, so the operation is performed as:

$$60.00 \text{ grams } CaCl_2 \text{ X } \frac{1 \text{ mol}}{110.98 \text{ gram}} = 0.5406 \text{ moles } CaCl_2$$

Next, the number of moles of $CaCl_2 \cdot 2H_2O$ that are needed to attain 0.5406 moles of $CaCl_2$ must be calculated. One mole of $CaCl_2 \cdot 2H_2O$ will produce one mole of $CaCl_2$ in solution, so their ratio is 1:1

$$0.5406 \text{ moles } CaCl_2 \text{ X } \frac{1 \text{ mol } CaCl_2 \cdot 2H_2O}{1 \text{ mol } CaCl_2} = 0.5406 \text{ moles } CaCl_2 \cdot 2H_2O$$

Finally, the mass of 0.5406 moles of $CaCl_2 \cdot 2H_2O$ can be calculated. $CaCl_2 \cdot 2H_2O$ has a molar mass of 147.01 g/mol, so the calculation is:

$$0.5406 \text{ moles } CaCl_2 \cdot 2H_2O \text{ X } \frac{147.01 \text{ g}}{1 \text{ mol}} = 79.48 \text{ grams } CaCl_2 \cdot 2H_2O$$

The three calculations we just performed can be summarized as:

$$60.00 \text{ grams } CaCl_2 \text{ X } \frac{1 \text{ mol}}{110.98 \text{ g}} \text{ X } \frac{1 \text{ mol } CaCl_2 \cdot 2H_2O}{1 \text{ mol } CaCl_2} \text{ X } \frac{147.01 \text{ g}}{1 \text{ mol}} = 79.48 \text{ grams } CaCl_2 \cdot 2H_2O$$

Making a 300.0 g/L $CaCl_2$ solution in a 200.00 mL volumetric flask will therefore require 79.48 grams of $CaCl_2 \cdot 2H_2O$.

[Handwritten at top: 1g NaCl in 10mL H₂O]

[Handwritten top right:]

$\underset{58.99\,g/mol}{NaCl} \Longleftarrow$ Na   Cl
22.99 + 35.45

He   O
1.008   16

$1\,g\,NaCl \times \dfrac{1\,mol}{58.44\,g} = \boxed{0.017\,mol}$ or NaCl

Calculating an Actual Solution Concentration

As you will discover, the solution you make in lab may actually contain a little more or a little less $CaCl_2 \cdot 2H_2O$ than the quantity you calculate will be needed. This is because weighing out precisely a given quantity of solid compound, although possible, can be difficult and an unnecessary waste of time in practice. It will therefore be necessary to use the mass of $CaCl_2 \cdot 2H_2O$ you actually weigh out to calculate the actual concentration of the solution you make. This will be true of any solution in you make in this course from solid chemical. As described in Appendix B, whenever you are instructed to measure out a quantity of reagent on a balance, it is permissible to precisely weigh out anything ±10% of the indicated or calculated quantity. In the case of our example, you could actually use anything between 71.53 grams and 87.43 grams of $CaCl_2 \cdot 2H_2O$ to make your solution.

[Handwritten: Molarity = $\dfrac{mol\ Solute}{Liter\ solution}$ $\dfrac{0.017\ mol\ NaCl}{0.01\ L} = 1.7\ mol/L$]

If you need to calculate the concentration of a calcium chloride solution given an amount of $CaCl_2 \cdot 2H_2O$, you can perform a calculation similar to the one used to determine the equivalent mass of $CaCl_2 \cdot 2H_2O$ from a mass of $CaCl_2$. This new calculation will essentially be the reverse of the earlier one.

For this example, let's assume that instead of the target quantity of 79.48 grams of $CaCl_2 \cdot 2H_2O$ calculated earlier, you actually weigh out 83.13 grams of $CaCl_2 \cdot 2H_2O$ for your 200.00 mL solution. The equivalent mass of $CaCl_2$ can be calculated as:

$$83.13 \text{ grams } \cancel{CaCl_2 \cdot 2H_2O} \times \frac{1\,\cancel{mol}}{147.01 \text{ g}} \times \frac{1 \text{ mol } CaCl_2}{1\,\cancel{mol\ CaCl_2 \cdot 2H_2O}} \times \frac{110.98 \text{ g}}{1\,\cancel{mol}} = 62.76 \text{ grams } CaCl_2$$

This number, 62.76 grams of $CaCl_2$ divided by the solution volume of 0.20000 L affords the solution's concentration in g/L: 313.78 g/L.

PROCEDURE CITATION

Begin your data and observations section for this experiment with a citation for the procedure you will follow. See the section on citing sources in the "Laboratory Report Guidelines" chapter for information on how to properly cite a source.

PROCEDURE

As you perform this experiment, make a note of all the equipment and chemicals you use. Give a brief description of the reagents used. Give the unit number on the balance you use. Use this same balance for all your mass measurements.

Most of the data you record in this lab will consist of numerical measurements. All your data must be clearly labeled so the reader can follow the numbers without referring to the procedures in the laboratory manual (see Laboratory Report Guidelines). Show all masses and volume measurements with the correct units and to the correct number of digits. Although most of your data will be numerical, be sure to make qualitative observations as you perform the experiment.

If you are unsure about any of the techniques used in this experiment, refer to Appendix A or B. If you are still unsure, ask your TA.

Part A: Preparation of a Calcium Chloride Stock Solution

1. Wash and thoroughly rinse with deionized water your volumetric flask, stir rod, funnel and a 150 mL beaker.

2. Your TA will provide you with a concentration for the calcium chloride solution you will make. Follow the guidelines provided in Appendix B to prepare a standard solution, of the concentration you were given, in your volumetric flask.

- Part of this procedure will require you to add a portion of $CaCl_2 \cdot 2H_2O$ to your weighing bottle. Fill your bottle to the same level (give-or-take) as the demo bottle in the hood; different demo bottles will be present for the different concentrations required. You can then use the weigh by difference technique as described in Appendix B to measure and calculate the amount of $CaCl_2 \cdot 2H_2O$ you actually use.

- It may help to warm your beaker a little on a hotplate to speed up the dissolving of the calcium chloride.

3. Use your flask size and weighing bottle mass data to calculate the actual concentration of the solution you just prepared in grams per liter (g/L).

- You will have to account for the waters of hydration in this calculation.

Part B: Density of a Calcium Chloride Solution

4. Clean and dry your weighing bottle. After you have ensured it is dry, determine its mass.

5. Follow the guidelines provided in Appendix B to rinse your volumetric pipette and ready it to dispense your calcium chloride solution (this is steps 1 and 2 of the instructions provided there).

6. Dispense an aliquot of your solution into your weighing bottle. Determine the mass of the weighing bottle with the solution in it.

16.30z

- "Aliquot" is defined in the pipette guidelines.

7. Repeat the previous steps until you have four sets of "empty bottle" and "bottle + solution" mass data.

8. Calculate the mass of liquid dispensed for each of your four trials.

9. There is an Excel file called "Lab Techniques" in the 105 folder on the computers in your lab room. Open it if it's not open already.

10. Enter your volume dispensed and fluid mass figures into the Lab Techniques spreadsheet and check your standard deviation. If it is more than 0.06 g/mL:

- Re-check the values you entered for entry mistakes

- If the values you entered are what you actually meant to enter, you may be using the pipette incorrectly. Review the guidelines provided in Appendix B, or ask your TA to demonstrate using it. Repeat all steps necessary to collect four more sets of mass data and enter your new values. Use these new values for all calculations in the Calculations section.

11. Write the average density the program returns and the actual concentration of your solution on the board in your lab room. Record this information from other students who were given other concentrations; you'll need three concentrations and their associated densities that differ from your own by at least 1.4 g $CaCl_2$/L. (Proceed with the following parts of this experiment if the other students are not done yet.)

Part C: Density of a Known Solution

For this part, your known liquid is deionized water. Its density is provided in the background.

12. Clean and dry your weighing bottle, then determine its mass. 11.73d

13. Rinse your pipette and ready it to dispense deionized water.

14. Use the pipette to dispense an aliquot of water into your weighing bottle. Determine the mass of the weighing bottle with the water in it. 24.56

15. Repeat the previous steps until you have four sets of "empty bottle" and "bottle + water" mass data.

16. Calculate the mass of liquid dispensed for each trial. Enter these figures into the spreadsheet and check your standard deviation. If it is more than 0.06 g/mL, re-check the values you entered for entry mistakes. If there are no such mistakes, repeat all steps necessary to collect four more sets of mass data, and then enter your new values. Use these for your calculations in the Calculations section.

Part D: Finishing Up

17. Rinse the inside of your weigh-bottle thoroughly with glass cleaning solution, then rinse three times with DI water.

POST-LAB: CALCULATIONS

Note: for all calculations that are repeated for separate trials, you must show a complete calculation at least once in your notebook. See the Laboratory Report Guidelines, "Calculations" for how to properly set up this section of your lab report. Make sure all numbers are labeled and have units.

Calcium Chloride Solution Density

1. Use the data collected for the calcium chloride solution to calculate its density. You will do this four times (one for each data set) and have four density figures when you finish.

2. Average the four calcium chloride solution density values.

3. Use the equation for the standard deviation provided in the background to calculate the standard deviation of the solution density figures. Although the computer program you used in lab calculated this for you, you still have to perform this calculation manually to demonstrate you can do so. You can use the value the computer provided to check your answer, though.

4. Calculate the range the standard deviation you just calculated falls around its average. Do this by subtracting one standard deviation from the average and adding one to the average.

Known Liquid Density

5. Use the data collected for the known liquid to calculate its density. (Again, four times.)

6. Average the four known liquid density values and calculate their standard deviation.

7. Calculate the range the standard deviation you just calculated falls around its average. (Add one standard deviation, and subtract one standard deviation to/from the average.)

POST-LAB: RESULTS AND DISCUSSION

The remaining requirements for your post-lab assignment will either be provided on-line or in a handout.

PROPERTIES OF ACIDS AND BASES

INTRODUCTION

The terms "acid" and "base" encompass a multitude of different compounds that have widely varying properties. Some of these are gentle and can be safely used around the home, while others are incredibly toxic and must be handled with the utmost care. Furthermore, the compounds within these sub-groups vary in the types of reactions they are capable of, and the applications they are suitable for. Vinegar and carbonic acid, for instance, could both be considered "gentle" acids, but only the latter is typically found in carbonated beverages (imagine what these beverages would taste like if they contained the former).

In this laboratory experiment, you will examine the properties of a selection of acids and bases. More specifically, you will observe what effect changing the type and/or concentration of acid or base has on a few different reactions. You will be expected to be familiar with acids and bases and their properties in future laboratory experiments and course work.

BACKGROUND

Acids

The Brønsted and Lowry definition of acids is that they are proton donors. By this definition, acids are easily identified because they produce a hydrogen ion (a proton) when dissolved in water. This hydrogen ion quickly reacts with water to form a hydronium ion, H_3O^+.

$$H^+(aq) + H_2O(l) \rightarrow H_3O^+(aq)$$

For convenience, we will typically use the symbol $H^+(aq)$ to represent the hydrogen ion and its concentration rather than the hydronium ion $H_3O^+(aq)$. However, it is important to remember that the terms $H^+(aq)$ and $H_3O^+(aq)$ are interchangeable in describing aqueous solutions and their calculations.

Categories of Acids

Acids can be categorized in multiple ways, such as whether they are inorganic or organic. Inorganic acids, which were covered in Worksheet 1, consist of an anion and a proton that can become dissociated from that anion. Hydrofluoric acid (HF), for instance, is an inorganic acid.

Organic acids, like inorganic acids, consist of an anion and a proton that can become dissociated from each other. However, unlike inorganic acid anions which *might* contain carbon, organic acid anions *always* contain carbon. As a general rule, an acid is considered organic if its anion consists of carbon, oxygen and hydrogen. Acetic acid, CH_3CO_2H, which dissociates into acetate ($CH_3CO_2^-$) and a proton, is a good example of an organic acid. One exception to this rule is carbonic acid, H_2CO_3. Although its anion, hydrogen carbonate (HCO_3^-, also called bicarbonate), clearly has a hydrogen, it is considered an inorganic acid. (It is worth noting that this second hydrogen can also dissociate, yielding the unprotonated CO_3^{2-} ion.)

Another way to categorize acids is by whether they are strong or weak. By definition, a weak acid is one that does not completely dissociate in solution; some acid molecules will dissociate to their respective H^+ and [anion]$^-$ components, but others will remain with the proton joined to the anion. Acetic acid is a weak acid. In a 1 molar solution of acetic acid, more than 99.5% of the molecules in solution will be in the non-dissociated form. By contrast, a strong acid will completely dissociate in solution.

There are only six strong acids, all of which are inorganic:

HCl	hydrochloric acid	HNO_3	nitric acid
HBr	hydrobromic acid	H_2SO_4	sulfuric acid (one proton)
HI	hydroiodic acid	$HClO_4$	perchloric acid

Acids have many different roles in a wide variety of situations. They are in many foods, particularly fruits, and are responsible for the sour taste of citrus fruits such as lemons and grapefruit. These naturally occurring acids are organic and weak. Some inorganic acids, such as the carbonic acid added to carbonated drinks, can also be found in foods. The acid in your stomach, hydrochloric acid, reacts with the food you eat and helps to break it down so nutrients can be absorbed. Acids also have many industrial roles: they can break down other compounds, speed-up otherwise slow synthesis reactions, and participate in the reactions in some batteries. One of the strong acids, sulfuric acid, is one of the most-produced chemicals in the world. Amongst other things, it is used in the production of fertilizer, detergents, pharmaceuticals, and pesticides.

In the laboratory, some acids are available as concentrated aqueous solutions while others are provided as a pure liquid. The most concentrated forms of sulfuric acid and acetic acid, for instance, are pure substances with no added water. Hydrochloric, hydrobromic, hydroiodic, and nitric acids on the other hand are always found as aqueous solutions because the acids themselves are gases.

Common and Chemical Names of Acids and Bases

Common Name	Chemical Names	Formula
muriatic acid	hydrochloric acid	HCl
oil of vitriol	sulfuric acid	H_2SO_4
baking soda	sodium hydrogen carbonate*	$NaHCO_3$
lye, caustic soda	sodium hydroxide	NaOH
magnesia	magnesium oxide	MgO
milk of magnesia	magnesium hydroxide	$Mg(OH)_2$
slaked lime	calcium hydroxide	$Ca(OH)_2$
potash†	potassium carbonate	K_2CO_3
caustic potash	potassium hydroxide	KOH
quicklime	calcium oxide	CaO
washing soda	hydrated sodium carbonate	$Na_2CO_3 \cdot 10H_2O$

*HCO_3^- is more commonly called bicarbonate, which would make $NaHCO_3$ sodium bicarbonate. However, hydrogen carbonate is the proper name for HCO_3^-.

†The name "potassium" is derived from the word "potash," from which the first samples of potassium where isolated.

Bases

A general definition for a base is that it is a substance that produces a hydroxide ion in water. This is why ammonia is a base.

$$NH_3(aq) + H_2O(l) \rightarrow NH_4^+(aq) + OH^-(aq)$$

Only inorganic bases will be considered in this laboratory experiment, though there are also many kinds of organic bases.

Both organic and inorganic bases are important industrial chemicals. Ammonia and sodium hydroxide, two inorganic bases, are among the top ten industrially produced chemicals. Around the home, bases are most commonly used as cleaning agents.

The most common bases are the soluble metal hydroxides, such as $NaOH$ and $Ca(OH)_2$. Other common bases are CaO, Na_2CO_3, $NaHCO_3$, and NH_3. Some strong bases, including $NaOH$ and KOH, are hydroxides of the alkali metal cations, which is the reason that older nomenclature uses the word alkaline to describe a basic solution.

As is the case with acidic solutions, basic solutions can degrade certain substances, including biological tissues. Many brands of drain cleaner, which use the strong base sodium hydroxide as an essential ingredient, take advantage of this property by breaking down hair and other materials that commonly clog drains. If you have ever made physical contact with a basic substance, you may notice that it feels slippery to the touch. This is because the base breaks the fats and oils of your tissues down into soap as it reacts with them. Many craft soaps are made in a similar reaction between lye (sodium hydroxide) and plant oils.

Reactions of Acids and Bases

Proton Transfer and Gas Formation

Volatile acids such as HCl are formed when an anion in an aqueous solution reacts with a proton, with the latter typically donated from another acid that is added to the solution. This reaction also occurs when a low volatility acid is added to a solid salt that contains the anion of the volatile acid. The added acid will dissolve some of the solid, allowing the ions to "swap partners". For instance, consider the reaction of sodium chloride with sulfuric acid. Note how the chloride ion becomes volatile $HCl(g)$ when it joints with a proton from H_2SO_4.

$$H_2SO_4(aq) + NaCl(s) \rightarrow NaHSO_4(s) + HCl(g)$$

When the hydrogen ion and the anion of a volatile acid combine in solution, the resultant volatile acid can leave the solution as a gas.

These reactions are also called proton transfer reactions because the proton from one acid is transferred to another anion to produce a different acid. When balancing these reactions or predicting the products from them, remember that opposite charges attract and that a cation will not associate with another cation, or an anion with another anion.

Neutralization

Neutralization reactions are some of the most commonly encountered ones in General Chemistry. In this type of reaction, an acid and a base react with each other to produce a salt (ionic compound) and water. When they react in stoichiometric quantities (no excess or limiting reactant), they will cancel out, or neutralize, their acidic and basic properties in aqueous solutions.

$$NaOH(aq) + HCl(aq) \rightarrow NaCl(aq) + H_2O(l)$$
$$\text{or}$$
$$Na^+(aq) + OH^-(aq) + H^+(aq) + Cl^-(aq) \rightarrow Na^+(aq) + Cl^-(aq) + H_2O(l)$$

The fact that the resulting solution is neither acidic (excess protons) nor basic (excess hydroxide ions) makes it very easy to detect when enough base has been added to an acidic solution to react with all the acid present, and vice-versa. (See "pH" below for a discussion of how excess protons and hydroxide ions are detected in aqueous solutions.)

Carbonate and Hydrogen Carbonates

Carbonates and hydrogen carbonates (bicarbonates), regardless of their associated cation, react with $H^+(aq)$ to form $CO_2(g)$. Since the reaction produces a gas, it is typical for both solid carbonates/hydrogen carbonates and aqueous solutions of them to effervesce when exposed to acid. An example of this is the reaction of limestone with sulfuric acid. It is because of this reaction that acid rain, which contains sulfuric acid, can damage buildings and statues that contain limestone or marble.

$$CaCO_3(s) + H_2SO_4(aq) \rightarrow CaSO_4(aq) + CO_2(g) + H_2O(l)$$

This reaction can also go in reverse when carbon dioxide gas is dissolved in water.

$$CO_2(g) + H_2O(l) \rightarrow HCO_3^-(aq) + H^+(aq)$$

Oxidation-Reduction

Oxidation-reduction, or redox, reactions are characterized by the movement of electrons from one compound to another. Because electrons are negatively charged, these movements result in charge changes to the elements involved. When an element gains an electron its charge decreases and so is said to be reduced. Conversely, when an element loses an electron, and so increases in positive charge, it is said to be oxidized. The reactant containing the element that becomes reduced is the oxidizing agent. Conversely, the reacting compound that contains the element that gets oxidized is the reducing agent.

The identity of any given reactant can sometimes be used to predict whether it will become oxidized or reduced in a reaction. For example, metals are commonly oxidized to their respective cations and halogens are reduced to halides. It is extremely difficult to reduce a metal to an anion or oxidize a halogen to a cation. However, metal cations can be reduced back to their elemental metal and halide anions can be oxidized back to their elemental form.

Example Oxidation and Reduction

Example	Oxidized or Reduced	Oxidizing or Reducing Agent	Charge Change
Calcium metal	oxidized	reducing agent	$Ca \rightarrow Ca^{2+}$
Fluorine gas	reduced	oxidizing agent	$F_2 \rightarrow F^-$
Silver nitrate	reduced	oxidizing agent	$Ag^+ \rightarrow Ag$
Sodium iodide	oxidized	reducing agent	$I^- \rightarrow I_2$
Acids	reduced	oxidizing agent	$H^+ \rightarrow H_2$

Oxidation of metals

Acids act as oxidizing agents when they react with metals to convert the metal atoms into ions. Like all oxidizing agents, they do this by removing electrons from metal. For most acids, it is the hydrogen ion that acts as the oxidizing agent; it is reduced to H_2 gas in the process:

$$Ca(s) + 2HCl(aq) \rightarrow Ca^{2+}(aq) + 2Cl^-(aq) + H_2(g)$$

For some other acids, the acid's anion moiety will participate in the reaction and become reduced. Nitric acid affords a good example of this. It is known as an oxidizing acid because its anion, nitrate, is a better oxidizing agent than the hydrogen ion. Because of this greater potential, nitric acid will react with metals that are inert to other acids.

The reaction of copper metal with nitric acid typifies the way this acid reacts with many other metals:

$$3Cu(s) + 8HNO_3(aq) \rightarrow 3\ Cu^{2+}(aq) + 6NO_3^-(aq) + 2NO(g) + 4H_2O(l)$$

When the colorless NO gas produced in this reaction reacts with O_2 in the air, it will become brown NO_2.

Oxidation of non-metals

Like nitric acid, concentrated sulfuric acid can also act as an oxidizing agent. In doing so, it will become reduced to SO_2 gas. For example, sulfuric acid can oxidize *some* (not all) halides such as the bromide ion (Br^-) to bromine, Br_2, per the following reaction. Note the differences between this reaction and the reaction of NaCl with H_2SO_4 described previously.

$$2NaBr(s) + 2H_2SO_4(aq) \rightarrow Br_2(l) + SO_2(g) + Na_2SO_4(aq) + 2H_2O(l)$$

Acid Reactions, General Considerations

Some of the oxidation-reduction reactions we have described are easily identified because the chemical change in the compound is accompanied by an observable physical change. In the case of bromine to bromide, a (usually) white, solid bromide salt becomes a brown liquid (elemental bromine). As mentioned, the reduction of nitrate in nitric acid ultimately leads to the production of brown NO_2 gas.

As you have likely gathered by now, any given acid could potentially participate in several different reactions with another compound: proton transfer, redox involving the acid's protons, or redox involving the acid's anion. Of these possibilities, which reaction occurs depends on the type of acid, its concentration, and its reaction partner. In this experiment, you will test the ability of a few different acids to act as an oxidizing agent when they react with different metals and halide salts. This will enable you to determine which of these compounds can and cannot be oxidized by different types and/or concentrations of acid.

pH

The pH of a solution is a measurement of the concentration of protons in it. The 'p' in front of the H is a math function that means "take the –log," thus

$$pH = -\log [H^+]$$

Square brackets around an ion or molecule is short hand for "concentration of;" the square brackets around H^+ means the concentration in molarity. Because the negative of the log is used, as the proton concentration increases, the calculated pH value decreases. Therefore acids, which produce protons in solution, have low pH values in the range of 0 to 5. Conversely, because H^+ concentrations decrease when OH^- concentrations increase, bases have higher pH values in the range of 8 to 14.

Indicators

Indictors are organic dyes that undergo pH-dependent color changes. There are many types of these, and different ones change from one color to another at different pHs. Two of the more common indicators are litmus and phenolphthalein. Litmus is a plant extract that is blue in basic solution and red in acidic solution. Red litmus is used to check whether a solution is basic, as indicated by a color change from red to blue. Blue litmus is used to check whether a solution is acidic, as indicated by a color change from blue to red. Neutral aqueous solutions that are neither acidic nor basic will leave the color of red and blue litmus unchanged. Phenolphthalein is an organic compound that will turn a basic solution bright pink, but remain colorless in an acidic solution.

Techniques

The following techniques will be used in this experiment to explore the properties of a few different acids and bases. Descriptions of each may be found in Appendix B.

Cleanliness   Estimating Amounts   Testing a Solution using Litmus Paper

Testing for an Acidic or Basic Gas

PROCEDURE CITATION

Begin your data and observations section for this experiment with a citation for the procedure you will follow. See the section on citing sources in the "Laboratory Report Guidelines" chapter for information on how to properly cite a source.

PROCEDURE

As you perform this experiment, record the procedure exactly as you perform it and make complete observations that are as detailed as reasonably possible. Your actual procedure may vary slightly each time you mix two solutions (a different number of drops added, for example). You must have a record of these deviations. The full description of any procedure only needs to appear once on EACH page in which there are data corresponding to that procedure.

Part A: Set Up

1. Clean all your test tubes and thoroughly rinse them with deionized water.

2. Some parts of this experiment will direct you to collect a certain amount of reagent in your test tubes before you begin. Collect these reagents and take them back to your bench to use in your tests; do not perform reactions at the main fume hood.

3. Reserve one of the beakers at your station for waste. As you perform this experiment, you can rinse your tubes and dishes into it. When you are done, empty the liquid portion of this waste into the main waste container in the fume hood. A separate container will be provided for solid waste.

Both dilute (dil) and concentrated (conc) acids and bases cause severe skin burns and irritation to the mucous membranes. Be careful in handling these chemicals.

Clean up all spills immediately. Refer to the "Laboratory Safety" section at the front of this manual and ask your TA if you have any questions.

Perform all of these reactions under your fume hood.

Never add water to concentrated acid.

Part B: Indicators

4. For parts B and C, you will need to collect <u>3 mL of each of the following</u>: 0.1 M HCl, 0.1 M HNO$_3$, 0.1 M H$_2$SO$_4$, and 0.1 M NaOH. To collect these, place three dropper-fulls of each into separate large test tubes.

    *   A "dropper-full" is what one fully squeezed bulb picks up; it is unlikely to actually fill the dropper.

5. Test each of the solutions you just collected with red and with blue litmus paper (as described in Appendix B).

6. Place between 10 and 15 drops of the NaOH into a small test tube. To this same tube, add 1-2 drops of phenolphthalein indicator and vortex to mix (Appendix B). Note the color of the resulting solution.

- You can use a Pasteur pipette to transfer the NaOH from the large tube to the small one.

Part C: Neutralization Reactions

7. NOTE: complete part B before you perform this part.

8. Place 10 drops of 0.1 M HCl into a small test tube, then add 1 drop of phenolphthalein indicator.

   - Again, you can use a Pasteur pipette for this transfer

9. Keeping track of how many drops you add, add individual drops of 0.1 M NaOH and mix the tube's contents by vortexing (Appendix B) after each drop. Note how many drops are required to cause a color change.

   - At the completion of this titration, the solution will be about the same color as the "NaOH + phenolphthalein" tube you made in the "Indicators" part.

10. Place 10 drops of 0.1 M HNO_3 into a small test tube and add 1 drop of phenolphthalein indicator. Titrate this tube as you did before and note how many drops are required to affect a color change.

11. Place 10 drops of 0.1 M H_2SO_4 and 1 drop of phenolphthalein into a small test tube. Again titrate as you did before.

12. Rinse your small tubes out with DI water when you are done

Part D: Reactions with $NaHCO_3$ and $Na_2C_2O_4$

13. Place a small quantity (about the size of an almond or a bean) of sodium hydrogen carbonate (i.e., sodium bicarbonate) into an evaporating dish. Place the same amount of sodium oxalate into a separate dish.

14. Add one dropper's worth* of 1.0 M H_2SO_4 to one of the dishes. Note any visible changes (bubbling, smoke formation, color changes, etc.) that occur to the dish's contents. When the reaction has finished, add a dropper of 1.0 M H_2SO_4 to the other dish and again observe.

    *The dropper does not have to be full, just what one fully squeezed bulb picks up

15. Clean the dishes out and set them up as you did before with solid $NaHCO_3$ and $Na_2C_2O_4$. Add acid to the salts as you did before, but use 1.0 M HCl instead of H_2SO_4.

Part E: Reactions with NaI and NaCl

> **CAUTION: 18 M H_2SO_4 is extremely caustic. Handle it with care.**

This part will utilize the "Testing for an Acidic or Basic Gas" technique described in Appendix B.

16. Collect about 2 dropper's worth of 18 M H_2SO_4 in a small tube and take it to your workstation for this part; don't perform the following reactions in the main hood where this acid is kept.

17. Place a small quantity (about the same amount of solid used for part D above) of NaI in a clean dry evaporating dish. Place the same amount of NaCl in a separate dish.

18. Moisten a piece of red and a piece of blue litmus paper with deionized water and stick them to the bottom (convex) side of a clean watch glass. Repeat so you have two watch glasses setup this way.

19. Place the watch glasses on top of the evaporating dishes so that the litmus papers are on the bottom of the glasses and exposed to the salts. (They will be above the salts, not touching them.)

> **Work under your fume hood for the next steps. Some of the gases produced here are noxious.**

20. Lift one of the watch glasses just enough to add one dropper's worth* of 3 M H_2SO_4 to the salt inside and then quickly replace it. Note the color of any gas that is produced and any other features of the reaction. Repeat for the other dish.

   *The dropper does not have to be full, just what one fully squeezed bulb picks up

21. Clean the dishes out and set them up as you did before with solid NaI and NaCl, and fresh pieces of litmus paper. Add acid to the salts as you did previously, but use concentrated (18 M) H_2SO_4 instead of 3 M.

   - You can use a Pasteur pipette to transfer the 18 M from its tube. When you are done, rinse the pipette thoroughly with DI water.

Your dishes may be somewhat hard to clean after this part. If this is the case, add some water to them, set them inside your fume hood, go on and complete the next part of this experiment, then clean them out.

Part F: Reaction with Solid Metal Samples

There are 6 sets of observations for this section; each of the three metals will be reacted with two acids. Note the details of any reaction that occurs, including whether heat is produced, the color of any gas that is produced, changes in the color of the solution and the appearance of the metal, the time it took for the changes to develop, and the time required for the reaction to stop.

22. Add one dropper of 6 M HCl* to each of three small test tubes.

   *The dropper does not have to be full, just what one fully squeezed bulb picks up.

23. Obtain two pieces each of Mg, Zn, and Cu metals and describe them.

24. Place one piece of Mg metal into one of the tubes, a piece of Zn metal into a second tube, and a piece of Cu metal in the third tube. Note what happens to each metal in these solutions.

25. Repeat this part, but use 6 M HNO_3 instead of 6 M HCl. Use fresh pieces of metal.

Part G: Dependence of Acid Concentration on Reaction Rates

26. Place 1 dropper's-worth of 6 M HCl, 1 M HCl, and 0.1 M HCl into three separate small test tubes.

27. Add one piece of Mg to each test tube. Observe for 5 minutes.

Part H: Clean-up

28. Decant the liquid portion of your waste beaker into the main waste container in the fume hood.

   - "Decant" means to pour off a liquid in such a way that you retain any solids that were in the same container as the liquid.

29. Deposit any metal scraps in your waste beaker in the metal waste beaker in the fume hood.

30. Put all used litmus paper in the garbage can.

   - Point penalties will be applied to your lab laboratory report if these are found in the sinks

31. Wash all your test tubes and stir rods with detergent, rinse with plenty of water, and place upside-down in the test tube rack to dry.

32. Wipe up any spills and dispose of any trash.

33. Check sink for litmus paper and metals. CAREFULLY remove any that are in the sink.

POST-LAB: RESULTS AND DISCUSSION

The requirements for your post-lab assignment will either be provided on-line or in a handout.

MOLAR MASS OF A KNOWN ACID

INTRODUCTION

If someone handed you an unknown solid crystalline compound and asked you to identify it, the task might seem overwhelming as there are thousands of different compounds that it could be. However, if you know the substance is an acid, then identifying it becomes easier because, from what you learned in the experiment "Acids and Bases," you now know something about the properties of acids. These properties can be used to help you further identify the acid.

One way to identify an unknown acid is to determine its molar mass. The molar mass of any compound, including an acid, can be calculated by taking the mass of a sample of that compound in grams and dividing by the number of moles present to provide the molar mass in grams per mole (g/mol). The mass of a sample is easy to determine—it can simply be weighed on a balance. The number of moles present, however, is usually somewhat trickier to obtain. This is where your knowledge of acids and bases comes into play.

The number of moles of acid in solution can be determined by making the acid react with a known quantity of base. This will be done by gradually adding a solution of the base to the acid solution until sufficient base has been added to react with all of the acid present. As you know from the experiment "Acids and Bases," if a pH indicator is present in the acidic solution the base is added to, then the point at which sufficient base has been added can be determined by a visual indication such as a color change. If the concentration of the base and the quantity of it used are both known, then the moles of it added can be calculated. Finally, the stoichiometry of its reaction with the acid can be used to calculate the moles of acid originally present. This summarizes the approach you will take in this lab to determine the number of moles of acid you are working with.

The technique you will use in this lab to measure out the base that will react with your acid is titration. Titrations are the precise and methodical addition of one reactant, the titrant, to another reactant, the sample. In this lab, your titrant will be a basic solution of sodium hydroxide.

This will be a two-part experiment in which you will perform your analytical technique on two different acids: a known acid and an unknown acid. These two analyses will be done over the course of two lab periods.

BACKGROUND

Acid-Base Titrations

A titration is an experimental technique in which a solution of known concentration is gradually and precisely added to a solution of unknown concentration until the reaction between the two solutions is complete. The point at which this reaction is "complete" is called the equivalence point and is defined as the point at which stoichiometric amounts of each reactant are present (no reactant is in excess). The stoichiometry depends on the chemical reaction that occurs during the titration, and can be determined from this reaction's balanced equation. In the case of acid-base titrations, the equivalence point occurs when the reaction mixture is neutralized; that is, the number of moles of $H^+(aq)$ ions from the acid equals the number of moles of $OH(aq)$ ions from the base.

The equivalence point of a titration is typically indicated by an observable change in the solution known as the endpoint. For an acid-base titration, this change is commonly provided by an indicator that is added to the sample solution. Indicators are pH-sensitive dyes that change color at a specific pH range. There are many types of these, and the pH range they change color in is different for each. In the case of a titration, it is desirable to choose one that will change color exactly at the pH of the equivalence point or as close to it as possible. If the identity of the acid and base are known, the pH range over which the equivalence point will be reached can be calculated and an appropriate indicator chosen. If either the acid or the base is unknown, a general purpose indicator can be used. The indicator used in this experiment is phenolphthalein. This indicator turns from colorless in acid to pink in base, more specifically around a pH of 8-9.

Stoichiometry and Molar Mass Calculations

As you may recall from the experiment "Acids and Bases," some acids contain more protons than others. Sulfuric acid, for instance, yields two protons per molecule, but nitric acid only one. Because this property can affect the stoichiometry of the acid-base reaction used in a titration, it will also affect the molar mass calculated for the acid titrated.

To illustrate the effect this has on a calculated molar mass, consider what would happen if 4.00 grams of two different acids, acid A and acid B, were brought into solution and titrated. Acid A is a monoprotic acid and Acid B is a diprotic acid; chemical symbols for these could therefore be represented as HA (acid A) and H_2B (acid B). Let's assume that both acid solutions require 17.0 mL of 1.00 M NaOH, or 0.0170 moles NaOH, to titrate them. Since each molecule of A reacts with one molecule of NaOH, and each molecule of B reacts with two of NaOH, the stoichiometry equations of these reactions would be written as:

$$\text{Acid A:} \qquad 0.0170 \text{ mol NaOH X } \frac{1 \text{ HA}}{1 \text{ NaOH}} = 0.0170 \text{ mol HA}$$

$$\text{Acid B:} \qquad 0.0170 \text{ mol NaOH X } \frac{1 \text{ H}_2\text{B}}{2 \text{ NaOH}} = 0.00850 \text{ mol H}_2\text{B}$$

The grams of acid A divided by the moles present affords a molar mass of 235 grams/mol. However, the grams of B divided by the moles present affords a molar mass of 470 grams/mol.

Equivalent Molar Mass

If the stoichiometry of an acid-base reaction is not known, it is still possible to perform this calculation to arrive at *a* molar mass of the acid. However, instead of providing the "true" molar mass of the acid, it will give a related figure instead: the acid's equivalent molar mass. The calculation of an equivalent molar mass is performed as the molar mass calculation above was, but with the assumption that the acid reacts with the base in a 1:1 ratio, regardless of whether it actually does or not. You may notice that, although this would have still provided the correct molar mass of acid A, the calculated molar mass of B would have been half of its true value.

Primary and Secondary Standards

As mentioned previously, the quantity and concentration of sodium hydroxide you add to your solution(s) of acid will enable you to calculate the concentration of that acid. Obviously, your ability to perform this calculation will depend upon first knowing the concentration of the sodium hydroxide solution. Ordinarily, this concentration could be calculated from the mass of sodium hydroxide used to make the solution of it and the final volume of that solution. However, because solid sodium hydroxide is hygroscopic, meaning it can accumulate water from the air around it, the mass of it that is used to make a solution cannot be accurately determined by weighing. Therefore, it will be necessary to determine its concentration another way.

The method you will use to determine the concentration of your sodium hydroxide solution will essentially be the same one you will use to determine the concentration of your acid: a titration. For this titration, you will use a solution of sodium hydroxide you do not know the concentration of to titrate a solution of acid you do know the concentration of. Note that this situation, using an acid of known concentration to determine the concentration of an unknown hydroxide solution, is the reverse of the situation described above. Because this particular acid's concentration will be accurately known, it is referred to as the primary standard of the titration.

Once its concentration has been determined, the sodium hydroxide solution, which is now the secondary standard, will be used to titrate a solution of the acid you are trying to determine the molar mass of. From this titration you will be able to calculate the number of moles of $H^+(aq)$ in the volume that was titrated. This information, along with the mass of acid that was used to make a solution of it, can be used to calculate the molar mass of the acid.

To summarize this approach, you will:

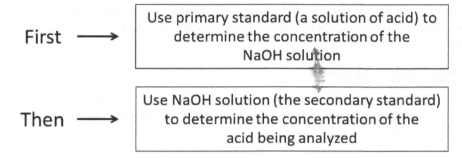

First ⟶ Use primary standard (a solution of acid) to determine the concentration of the NaOH solution

Then ⟶ Use NaOH solution (the secondary standard) to determine the concentration of the acid being analyzed

If titrating the two different acids in this way still seems strange, think of the first acid (the primary standard) as a tool that is used to "calibrate" the NaOH solution.

Known and Unknown Acids

This experiment will actually consist of two semi-separate experiments that will be performed in two different lab periods. The first of these sub-experiments will involve the titration of a known acid of known molar mass, which will act as a control. The results of this first titration will enable you to evaluate the accuracy of your technique. The second sub-experiment will be performed on an unknown acid of unknown molar mass. Your objective in this latter case is to determine the unknown acid's molar mass. Overall, this sequence of titrations can be depicted as follows. Note that, because the two parts of this experiment will be done in two different weeks, you will have to titrate the primary standard twice.

Week 1:

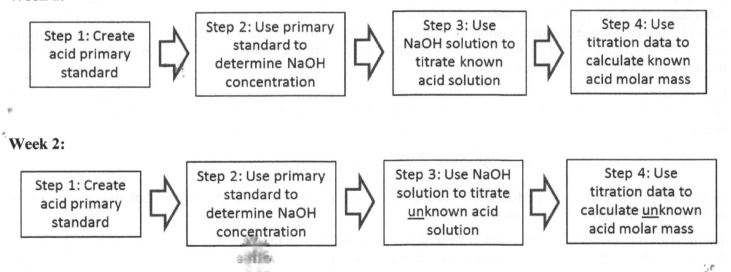

Step 1: Create acid primary standard ⟹ Step 2: Use primary standard to determine NaOH concentration ⟹ Step 3: Use NaOH solution to titrate known acid solution ⟹ Step 4: Use titration data to calculate known acid molar mass

Week 2:

Step 1: Create acid primary standard ⟹ Step 2: Use primary standard to determine NaOH concentration ⟹ Step 3: Use NaOH solution to titrate unknown acid solution ⟹ Step 4: Use titration data to calculate unknown acid molar mass

Standard Solutions

The acid you will use to create your primary standard will be prepared by dissolving the solid form of it in a volumetric flask (see Appendix B for the procedure). Solutions that are prepared in this way that have accurately known concentrations are sometimes called standard solutions. A volumetric pipette (again, see Appendix B) will then be used to dispense a specific volume of this solution into a flask so it can be titrated with the sodium hydroxide solution.

Calculations

This experiment will require you to perform several different calculations to determine the concentration of the NaOH and the molar masses of the known and unknown acids from your titration data. These calculations will include unit conversions, which will themselves require that you understand how to work with units. Be aware that the example calculations provided here only represent one method of arriving at the desired result when beginning from an initial set of numbers.

Concentrations and Molar Masses

The calculation of a solution concentration in moles per liter is a straightforward operation provided the quantity of solute in that solution and its volume are both known: the number of moles of solute is divided by the volume of the solution in liters.

$$\text{Concentration of a solution in moles/liter} = \frac{\text{Moles of solute}}{\text{Volume of solution in liters}}$$

If the concentration of the solution must be calculated in moles per liter but the quantity of solute is only known in grams, it will be necessary to first use the molar mass of the solute to convert the amount present in grams to moles.

The calculation of a molar mass is similarly straightforward if the grams of a sample and the number of moles present in that sample are both known:

$$\text{Molar mass of a compound} = \frac{\text{Grams of compound}}{\text{Moles of compound}}$$

Calculation of a Sodium Hydroxide Solution Concentration

You will be asked to calculate the concentration of a solution of NaOH as part of your experimental analysis. Although it will be possible to obtain a volume of NaOH from which make this calculation, it will not be possible to directly measure the number of moles of NaOH in that volume. Instead, you will have to indirectly determine the moles of NaOH present by its reaction with a known quantity of acid. The following example demonstrates how this can be done.

Let's assume that 15.67 mL of NaOH are required to completely neutralize all of the acid present in 20.00 mL of a 3.50 molar diprotic acid solution. In order to determine the molarity of the NaOH solution, it will first be necessary to determine how many moles of acid were in the 20.00 mL of it used:

$$0.02000 \, \text{L} \times \frac{3.50 \text{ moles acid}}{\text{L}} = 0.0700 \text{ moles acid}$$

Note how this operation is performed to cancel liters and provide moles. Also note that the conversion of 20.00 mL to 0.02000 L is not depicted.

The next step is to calculate the number of moles of NaOH that reacted with the 0.0700 moles of acid. This is done by applying the reaction stoichiometry. Since we are working with an unspecified diprotic acid, we can represent it as H_2A. It being diprotic, NaOH would react with this acid in a 2:1 ratio.

$$0.0700 \text{ moles acid } (H_2A) \times \frac{2 \text{ NaOH}}{1 \, H_2A} = 0.140 \text{ moles NaOH}$$

Now that we know the number of moles of NaOH that were in the 15.67 mL of it used, we can calculate the concentration of the NaOH solution by dividing this number of moles by the volume. Of course, since this volume is in milliliters but molarities are given in moles per liter, it will first be necessary to convert 15.67 mL to liters. If you do these calculations for yourself, you should arrive at a concentration of 8.93 M for the NaOH.

Calculation of a Known or Unknown Acid Molar Mass

Once the concentration of an NaOH solution is known, it can be used to determine the molar mass of a known or unknown acid via a titration experiment. The overall approach to this is:

1. Make a solution of the acid from a known mass of it
2. Determine the concentration of the acid solution
3. Calculate how many total moles are present in the solution
4. Use the mass and total moles of acid present to calculate its molar mass

For the following example, we will assume a solution of unknown acid was prepared by dissolving 79.89 grams of the acid into 200.00 mL of solution.

After the acid solution has been made, the next step is to determine the molarity of this solution. This process is basically the reverse of the calculations used to determine the concentration of NaOH in the previous example. To illustrate this process, let's say 13.41 mL of the NaOH solution we previously determined the concentration of is required to neutralize 25.00 mL of the acid solution. We can begin by calculating the number of moles of NaOH that were used for this:

$$0.01341 \text{ L} \times \frac{8.93 \text{ moles NaOH}}{\text{L}} = 0.120 \text{ moles NaOH}$$

Once the number of moles of NaOH is known, the reaction stoichiometry can then be used to determine the number of moles of acid that reacted with them. If we are doing this for an unknown acid, we would assume they react in a 1:1 ratio as follows (the acid is represented as HA):

$$.120 \text{ moles NaOH} \times \frac{1 \text{ HA}}{1 \text{ NaOH}} = 0.120 \text{ moles HA}$$

Of course, if the identity of the acid were known, we would use its actual reaction stoichiometry in this calculation, which may or may not be 1:1.

Now that the number of moles of acid that were present in the 25.00 mL of it used is known, we can calculate the concentration of the unknown acid solution. If you do this for yourself, you should arrive at a concentration of 4.80 M.

As for any solution, if the concentration and volume of our acid solution are both known, we can calculate how many moles of acid are present that solution. Since the total volume of the solution is 200.00 mL, this calculation would be:

$$0.20000 \text{ L} \times \frac{4.80 \text{ moles acid}}{\text{L}} = 0.960 \text{ moles acid}$$

Now that we know 0.960 moles of acid were present in the 79.89 grams of it used, we can calculate its molar mass. Since we are performing this calculation on an unknown acid, this number will actually be its *equivalent* molar mass. If you perform it yourself, you will find our unknown acid has an equivalent molar mass of 83.2 grams/mol.

Techniques

This lab will utilize some of the techniques introduced in the experiment "Laboratory Techniques and Measurements", the procedures for which are given in Appendix B. Poor laboratory technique and misuse of the glassware will result in poor data, which will affect the grade you receive on the laboratory report. In order to use your time efficiently in lab, review the following Appendix B topics:

rinsing glassware	preparation of a standard solution	use of a volumetric pipette
weighing by difference	set up and use of a burette	

PROCEDURE CITATION

Begin your data and observations section for this experiment with a citation for the procedure you will follow. See the section on citing sources in the "Laboratory Report Guidelines" chapter for information on how to properly cite a source.

PROCEDURE

Most of the data you record in this lab will consist of numerical measurements, though you will also make some qualitative observations as well. You will do a minimum of three titrations of the oxalic acid solution, and three of the un/known acid solution.

As you perform this experiment, make a note of all the equipment and chemicals you use. Be sure to include the size of all volumetric glassware and give a description of all the reagents you use.

Part A: Preparation of the Primary Standard

Unless instructed otherwise, you will use oxalic acid, a diprotic acid, as your primary standard.

1. Calculate the quantity of $H_2C_2O_4 \cdot 2H_2O$ needed for the size of your volumetric flask in order to prepare a solution of $H_2C_2O_4$ that is approximately 0.05 M. Have your TA initial your value before you continue.

2. Wash and thoroughly rinse with deionized water your volumetric flask, stir rod, funnel and a 150 mL beaker.

3. Follow the guidelines provided in Appendix B to prepare a standard solution of approximately 0.05 M oxalic acid in your volumetric flask.

Part B: Titration of Oxalic Acid

4. Obtain about 40 mL of NaOH solution in a clean dry beaker. Use a portion of it to rinse your burette (see "rinsing glassware" in Appendix B).

5. Clamp the burette in a burette clamp and place a waste beaker below it. Follow the remaining guidelines as provided in Appendix B to prepare it for dispensing the NaOH solution.

    *   Note that a portion of the credit you will receive for your burette data will depend on reading it correctly and making appropriate initial and final readings.

6. Rinse your volumetric pipette with your oxalic acid solution twice, discarding the rinse solution. (You can pour some of the acid into a clean dry beaker first to make this easier.)

7. Use your pipette to dispense aliquots of the acid solution into each of four different clean 250 mL Erlenmeyer flasks. (The flasks don't have to be dry, but they do have to be clean.)

8. Add two drops of phenolphthalein indicator to each flask.

9. Titrate the acid in one of the four flasks quickly, swirling the Erlenmeyer flask as you add the base from the burette. Stop adding base when the solution in the flask turns and stays pink. A piece of white paper placed underneath the flask will make the endpoint more visible.

    *   This first titration is considered a "rough" titration. It is done quickly to get an approximation of the endpoint.

10. Now that you have finished your rough titration, you should practice dispensing partial drops from your burette before you proceed. (Trying to properly titrate something without knowing how to add partial drops can be a downright agonizing experience.) You can use the same flask you used for your rough titration to practice these (no need to clean it out).

- To add a partial-drop, very slowly open your burette's stopcock until you can just see a droplet begin to form on the end of its spout, then turn the stopcock off. You can use your wash bottle to rinse this droplet off the spout and into your flask. Alternatively, you can touch the inside of the flask to the droplet and use the bottle to rinse it down the flask's side and into the solution. Try both techniques and use whichever you find easier.

- When you can reliably add a partial drop several times in a row without accidently dispensing a full drop (or more), proceed to the next step.

11. Refill the burette and again prepare it for dispensing.

12. Take another one of the flasks prepared with oxalic acid and phenolphthalein and add all but approximately 1 mL of the volume of NaOH that was needed to titrate the first sample to it. Swirl the flask and make sure the pink color fades.

   - If the color does not fade, repeat this step with another prepared flask, except add all but 2 mL of the NaOH volume.

13. Continue to add NaOH one drop—or half or quarter-drops—at a time until you reach the titration's endpoint. Swirl the flask in between each addition of NaOH.

   - Note: as you get close to the endpoint, the magenta/pink color will take more time to fade away (not a lot of time, but it will take noticeably longer for it to fade). When you get to this point, add half or quarter drops instead of full ones. Remember to rinse any partial drops down the sides of your flask and into your solution when you do this.

   - The endpoint will be a pale pink color, visible only against a white background. Have your TA verify that you have the proper endpoint color. Although this color may fade with time, the titration is considered complete when the solution remains pink for at least 30 seconds. Have your TA initial the final and initial burette readings of the titration for which the endpoint was verified.

14. Titrate your remaining flasks as you did the previous one. By the time you have finished, you will have a total of three flasks that were titrated by the "careful" titration method.

   - If you accidently flubbed one or more of your "careful" titrations by overshooting the amount of NaOH added to it, you will have to prepare more flasks with acid and phenolphthalein and titrate those.

15. Open the Excel file named "Titration" in the 105 folder on your computers desktop. Enter your oxalic acid and burette data into this and note the standard deviation it provides you.

16. If your standard deviation is larger than 0.06 mL, you may be using the pipette or burette incorrectly. Review their usage as explained in Appendix B, and then prepare three more flasks as you did at the beginning of part B. Titrate these flasks, enter your data into the computer, and note the standard deviation.

   - Use the data from these new titrations for all subsequent calculations.

   - If your standard deviation is still more than 0.06 mL after the second round, proceed to the next step anyway.

17. Deposit all leftover oxalic acid solution in the lab's waste container and carefully clean the volumetric flask. Leave the burette set-up with NaOH.

Part C: Titration of the Known Acid

18. For this part, you will titrate a known acid of known molecular weight, which will act as a control for this experiment. Be sure to note the acid's molar mass, and whether it is monoprotic, diprotic, or triprotic. An indication to this effect will be on the bottle.

19. Clean and dry your weighing bottle. After you have ensured it is dry, put some of the known acid into it; use the same volume of known acid as you used for the oxalic acid previously.

20. Use the same technique you used in part A to make a standard solution of the acid. Use whatever mass of acid you collected in the previous step.

   • Note: it is very important that both your beaker and your volumetric flask be thoroughly clean before you do this.

21. Titrate the known acid solution as you did the oxalic acid solution (with a "rough" and three "good" or "careful" titrations). Again, enter your titration data into the computer. Again, if your standard deviation is more than 0.06 mL, perform three more titrations.

Part D: Clean Up

22. Deposit all remaining solutions and solids in the lab's waste container.

23. Wash all glassware with detergent, rinse with plenty of water, and lay out to dry on your towel.

24. Clean up any spills and throw away garbage

POST-LAB: CALCULATIONS
Part A

1. Calculate the actual concentration in moles/L of the oxalic acid primary standard you created in part A.

Part B

2. Calculate the concentration in moles/L of the sodium hydroxide solution you worked with.

   • The "Calculations" section in the background contains an example of the calculations this will require.

   • You will have to calculate this concentration three times using the data from your three "careful" titrations in turn.

3. Average the NaOH concentrations you just calculated.

4. Use the equation for the standard deviation provided in the experiment "Laboratory Techniques" to calculate the standard deviation of your NaOH concentrations.

5. Calculate the range your standard deviation falls around your average NaOH concentration by adding one standard deviation to this average and subtracting one from it.

Part C

6. Use your titration data to calculate the molar mass of the known acid you titrated in part C.

   • The background contains an example of how this calculation can be done.

   • You will have to perform this calculation three times using the data from your three "careful" part C titrations in turn.

   • Use the average NaOH concentration you calculated previously for these calculations.

7. Average the molar masses you calculated for the known acid.

8. Calculate the standard deviation of the molar masses for the known acid.

9. Calculate the range your standard deviation falls around the average by adding one standard deviation to this average and subtracting one from it.

POST-LAB: RESULTS AND DISCUSSION

The remaining requirements for your post-lab assignment will either be provided on-line or in a handout.

MOLAR MASS OF AN UNKNOWN ACID

INTRODUCTION

This lab is a continuation of the "Molar Mass of a Known Acid" experiment. Here, you will determine the molar mass of an unknown acid. The background provided for the "Molar Mass of a Known Acid" chapter applies to this experiment as well.

PROCEDURE

The procedure you follow for this part of the experiment will be the same one used in the "Molar Mass of a Known Acid" experiment. The only difference is you will create a solution of unknown acid instead of known acid in part C of the procedure. Your TA will assign one of the unknown acids to you.

POST-LAB: CALCULATIONS

The parts referred to here correspond to those in the "Molar Mass of a Known Acid" experiment.

Part A

1. Calculate the actual concentration of the primary standard you created in part A in moles/L.

Part B

2. Calculate the concentration of the sodium hydroxide solution you worked with in moles/L.

    *   The "Calculations" section in the background to the experiment "Molar Mass of a Known Acid" contains an example of the calculations this will require.

    *   You will have to calculate this concentration three times using the data from your three "careful" titrations in turn.

3. Average the NaOH concentrations you just calculated.

4. Use the equation for the standard deviation provided in the experiment "Laboratory Techniques" to calculate the standard deviation of your NaOH concentrations.

5. Calculate the range your standard deviation falls around your average NaOH concentration by adding one standard deviation to this average and subtracting one from it.

Part C

6. Calculate the molar mass of the acid you titrated in part C.

    *   Assume the acid reacts with NaOH in a 1:1 ratio.

    *   You will have to calculate this three times using the data from your three "careful" part C titrations in turn.

    *   Use the average NaOH concentration you calculated previously for these calculations.

7. Average the molar masses you calculated for the unknown acid.

8. Calculate the standard deviation of the molar masses for the unknown acid.

9. Calculate the range your standard deviation falls around the average by adding one standard deviation to this average and subtracting one from it.

POST-LAB: RESULTS AND DISCUSSION

The remaining requirements for your post-lab assignment will either be provided on-line or in a handout.

IDENTIFICATION OF A METAL

INTRODUCTION

The "Laboratory Techniques and Measurements" experiment introduced you to a technique for determining the density of a solution. Although that experiment involved working with a liquid, a related technique can be used to calculate the density of solid object. Since the densities of different types of solids vary, determining the density of a solid object can help you identify what that object is.

Although knowing the density of an object is useful, it does have limitations. As you might have seen in the "Techniques" experiment, because of the error inherent in all measurements, if two objects, phenomena, etc. are too similar, any measurements taken of them may not be significantly different from each other. If the densities of two objects are close in value, it therefore might not be possible to tell them apart. For this reason, if you are trying to determine what an object is, it is useful to have a second means of analyzing it. In this experiment, you will be provided with such a means by learning a new technique you can use to help identify substances.

The new technique you will learn in this experiment is basically a way of analyzing the ability of matter to store a certain kind of energy, which can be determined by measuring the temperature changes matter undergoes as it heats up and cools down. Ultimately, you will use this new technique to identify an unknown metal. To help you understand what temperature changes have to do with energy storage, we will begin with a discussion of what exactly temperature and heat have to do with each other.

BACKGROUND

Temperature

Temperature is one of the most commonly encountered types of measurement in our daily lives. For instance, we often use it to describe how "hot" or "cold" it is outside. What exactly does it mean, though, for an object to be at a certain temperature? That is, what is it about the air in a room that makes that room 21°C? What happens to the water in a glass to make that water 4°C? To answer these questions, we need to first take a look at what the air or water molecules are doing as they occupy the room or glass.

Unless the temperature of a sample of matter is at absolute zero (the coldest temperature anything can ever achieve under any circumstances), the atoms and molecules that makeup that matter are always in motion. If you could see the molecules of gas that makeup the air around you, you would find that they are always moving around and colliding what whatever they happen to run into, be it the wall of a room, your body, or each other. The speed with which they do this is in turn related to how much energy they have, more energy resulting in more speed.

The concept of energy is itself somewhat abstract. It is commonly defined as the capacity to do work. However, if you are not satisfied with that definition or find it ambiguous, you can think of it this way instead: energy is what is needed to make things move. A ball moving across a table, for instance, has a certain amount of energy associated with it, and it can transfer that energy to another ball by striking it. As soon as it does so, the second ball will start moving. Air molecules in motion can do something similar to other air molecules.

Coming back to our original question, the temperature of air, water, or any other object is an indirect measurement of the energy of the molecules that make it up. Air molecules at a higher temperature will have a higher energy, and therefore move faster, than those at a lower temperature. Something similar is also true of liquids, and even of solid substances. In the case of the solids, the molecules that make them up do move, but these motions tend to resemble vibrations rather than the motions of a liquid or gaseous molecule (if the molecules were completely free to move about, the object wouldn't be a solid).

Heat

Like temperature, heat is a fairly commonly-encountered word. If a room is cold, someone might ask that the heat be turned up. If it's a hot day in August, someone else may comment on heat outside. These usages, however, differ somewhat from the scientific definition of heat.

Scientifically speaking, heat is a *transfer* of energy from an object at one temperature to another object at a different temperature. This transfer will cause the temperatures of those objects to change. That of the higher-temperature object will become lower, and that of the lower-temperature object will become higher.

Heat Transfers in Systems and their Surroundings

Typically, when studying the flow of energy as heat to or from an object of interest, that object is referred to as the system. Since objects will exchange energy as heat with everything that surrounds them, everything around the object is referred to as the surroundings.

A short-hand notation system is used to refer to heat and the transfers it undergoes. Heat itself is given the symbol q. For situations in which energy as heat flows from the surroundings to the system, q is considered to be a positive quantity. Conversely, when energy as heat flows from the system to the surroundings, q is considered to be a negative quantity.

If it helps you keep these signs straight, you could think of the system as gaining or losing energy whenever a heat exchange occurs to it. Since a gain of energy suggests an addition, it makes sense q would be a positive number when energy flows to the system. A loss, or subtraction, of energy from the system would in turn signify a negative q.

Processes in which there is a net transfer of energy as heat from the surroundings to the system—those with a +q—are called endothermic processes. If the process is a chemical reaction, it will be referred to as an endothermic reaction. Those in which there is a net transfer of energy as heat from the system to the surroundings—those with a –q—are called exothermic processes/reactions.

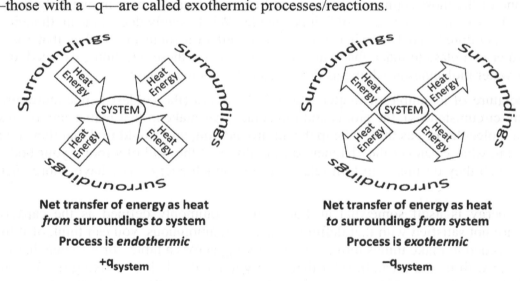

Net transfer of energy as heat
from surroundings *to* system

Process is *endothermic*

$+q_{system}$

Net transfer of energy as heat
to surroundings *from* system

Process is *exothermic*

$-q_{system}$

Since the temperature of matter is related to its energy "content," whenever that matter gains or loses energy as heat by an endo- or exothermic process it's temperature will rise or fall respectively. The following equation is used to relate the flow of energy as heat to/from a system to the temperature change that system undergoes as a result of the heat:

$$q = C \times \Delta t \qquad OR \qquad q = C \times (t_{final} - t_{initial})$$

Where q is the quantity of energy as heat the system absorbs or evolves, Δt is the change in temperature the system undergoes (final temperature – initial temperature), and C is the system's heat capacity, which is a measurement of how much heat the system must absorb or evolve for its temperature to change by 1°C.

Example Calculation

Let's say we have an object with a heat capacity of 478 J/°C. The object is initially at a temperature of 22.8°C, it absorbs energy as heat until its temperature is 42.3°C, and we need to know how much energy as heat it absorbs. The equation would be setup as:

$$q = 478 \text{ J/°C} \times (42.3°C - 22.8°C)$$

If you solve for q, you will find it equals 9320 J. Note that it calculated as a positive number, indicating an endothermic, energy-absorbing process.

Specific Heat

The heat capacity of matter is itself equal to two things: the mass (think "amount") of matter present, and that matter's specific heat, which is a constant specific to that type of matter. These are related as follows:

$$C = c \times m$$

Where m is the mass of the matter/object, c is its specific heat, and C is the matter's total heat capacity. This equation can be combined with the previous one as follows:

$$q = c \times m \times \Delta t \qquad \text{OR} \qquad q = c \times m \times (t_{final} - t_{initial})$$

Example Calculation

Like any equation, if you know all but one of the parameters in this one, you can solve for the remaining unknown parameter. Let's say we want to know the specific heat of a type of rock. A sample of this rock—the system—with a mass of 25.6 grams absorbs 787 J of energy. The initial and final temperature of the rock is 32.7°C and 43.1°C respectively. The equation would therefore be setup as:

$$787 \text{ J} = c \times 25.6 \text{ g} \times (43.1°C - 32.7°C)$$

Solving for c, this rock has a specific heat of 2.96 J/g·°C

Determining the Specific Heat of a Metal

Since different substances have different specific heats, an unknown substance can be identified by performing an experiment to determine its specific heat. In this experiment, you will do this for an unknown metal.

The easiest way to use the above equation to determine the specific heat of a metal would be to measure that metal's temperature, apply or extract a specific quantity of energy as heat to/from it, and measure its temperature again. However, since we have no device that can directly apply a specific, measurable amount of heat to a sample of metal, there is no practical way to do this in your lab. Furthermore, it is difficult to directly measure that metal's temperature with the probes we have available.

To get around these problems, you will first heat your metal sample up to a known temperature, then immerse it in a sample of water. When the metal makes contact with the water, it will transfer heat energy to the water until their temperatures are the same. Since the specific heat of water, 4.18 J/g·°C, is known, you will be able to calculate how much energy as heat the metal transferred to it. The following example will illustrate how this can be done.

Example Calculation

First, the sample of metal will be heated up to a known temperature. This can be done by immersing it in a beaker of boiling water and measuring the temperature of that water. Given sufficient time, the temperature of the metal will equal that of the water around it. Let's assume our metal has a mass of 8.78 grams and is put into water at 97.3°C.

- Note: the temperature probes you will use are sensitive enough you may find the temperature of your water appears to move up and down a little. If this is the case, take four consecutive temperatures and average them. The important thing is that the temperature of the water does not trend up or down.

Next, the metal will be placed into a second container of water that is initially at room temperature. Because the metal is hotter than this water, there will be a net transfer of energy from the metal to the water. As a result, the water's temperature will increase and that of the metal will decrease until they are both at the same temperature. Since their final temperatures are the same, you can determine the final temperature of the metal by measuring the final temperature of the water. Let's say 45.2 mL of water was used for this. It was initially at 22.7°C and rose to a temperature of 29.4°C.

- Note: as you will discover below, the final temperature of your water will be calculated from a plot. We're skipping this part for now to focus on the specific heat calculation.

Since the quantity of water used is in mL but the equation requires it to be in grams, we will have to convert 45.2 mL to g:

$$45.2 \; \text{mL water} \; \times \; 1.00 \frac{\text{g}}{\text{mL}} \; = 45.2 \; \text{g water}$$

The initial temperature, final temperature, and mass of the water can now be used to determine how much energy as heat the water absorbed. This is done by inserting the temperatures, mass, and specific heat of water into the above equation as follows:

$$q_{water} = 4.18 \; \text{J/g·°C} \; \times \; 45.2 \; \text{g} \; \times \; (29.4°C - 22.7°C)$$

$$q_{water} = 1270 \; \text{J (or 1.27 kJ)}$$

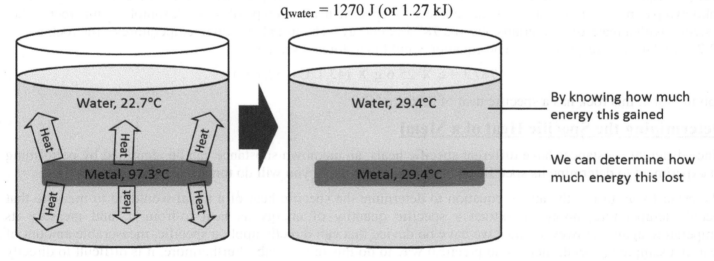

Since all of the energy absorbed by the water (q_{water}) evolved from the metal, the value of q for the metal (q_{metal}) will be equal in magnitude but opposite in sign to q_{water}:

$$q_{water} = -q_{metal}$$

In a more generic sense, this could also be written as:

$$q_{surroundings} = -q_{system}$$

Since q_{water} was 1270 J, q_{metal} is -1270 J.

Now that we know how much energy as heat the metal evolved, its final and initial temperatures and mass can be used to calculate its specific heat. The equation for this would be setup as:

$$-1270 \text{ J} = c \ \text{X} \ 8.78 \text{ g} \ \text{X} \ (29.4°C - 97.3°C)$$

If you solve for c, you will find this metal has a heat capacity of 2.13 J/g·°C.

Calorimetry and Calorimeters

The procedure we just outlined, in which the heat lost or gained by a system is determined by measuring the heat gained or lost by its immediate surroundings, describes the basic theory of calorimetry.

Whenever calorimetry is used to measure the heat gained or lost by a system, the water in that system must be isolated from everything else around it. If it isn't, the water would lose or gain heat to the air in the lab room and the bench it sits on. For this reason, these experiments are conducted in insulated vessels called calorimeters. The calorimeter you will use in this experiment will consist of two insulated coffee cups nestled together:

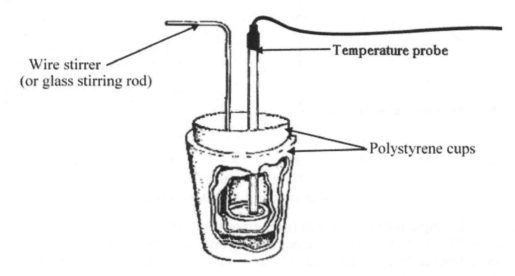

<u>Measurement of Temperature Changes</u>

Intuitively, it may seem that the water's temperature change can be measured by simply recording an initial temperature, adding the metal, and then taking a final temperature reading. However, this approach will not work in this experiment. This is because the temperature change of the water is not instantaneous; there will be a lag from the time the metal is added to the time the water's temperature has stopped rising or falling. Unfortunately, the calorimeter you will use is not a perfect insulator, so while you are waiting for the temperature reading to finish changing and stabilize, some heat will be lost to, or absorbed from, the various things around the calorimeter (air in the room, lab bench, etc.). If the water's temperature becomes higher than the temperature of your lab room, it will tend to lose energy as heat to the room. Because of this, the highest temperature you record would not be the highest temperature that the water would have achieved if its temperature change had been instantaneous and it didn't have a chance to lose any heat. However, it is this theoretical temperature change that we are really interested in.

To overcome this problem, you will take temperature and time data, plot these data, and then use best-fit lines (described in the Laboratory Report Guidelines) to determine the change in temperature at the exact time the metal was added, as if the process were instantaneous. One best-fit line will be used to determine the initial temperature, and another to determine the final temperature. Each will be extrapolated to the time the metal is added, so they overlap at this time. In this way, the desired "theoretical temperature change" described above can be read from the y-axis of the plot. The following example will show you how this can be done.

Figure 6.1 Temperature versus time data for an exothermic process in a calorimeter. Temperature data was taken every ½ minute for 3 minutes before the hot metal was added the calorimeter, and then for another five minutes. The dashed best-fit line is for the before addition data, while solid best-fit line is for the after addition data. Note that the temperature reading at 4 minutes (the maximum measured temperature) is lower than the value of the after-addition line at the time of addition (marked by an X).

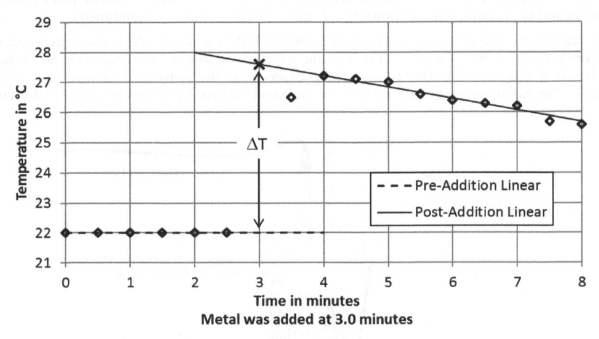

In the case of the example graph, note that the temperature of the dashed line is 22.0°C at 3 minutes, and that of the after addition line is 27.6°C at this same time point. The difference between these two temperatures, 5.6°C, is the change in water temperature at the time of metal addition. This is the Δt that will be used in the "$q_{water} = c \times m \times \Delta t$" equation to determine the energy as heat the water gains from the metal.

PROCEDURE

Part A: The Heat Capacity of a Known Metal Slug

1. Fill a 250 mL beaker about half-full of DI water. Use your hotplate to heat the water up to boiling or nearly so. When it starts to boil, turn it down so it just simmers. You can do the next few steps while you're waiting for it to boil.

2. Open the "Heat of Reaction" Logger Pro file in the 105 folder. A pop-up window may appear titled "Sensor Confirmation." Select "connect" if it does.

   • If the program and probe are working correctly, a temperature reading of somewhere between 19°C and 26°C will be indicated on the bottom left of your screen. If not, tell your TA.

3. Add 35-40 mL of DI water to your calorimeter (the two coffee cups nestled together).

4. Fill a second 400 mL beaker nearly full of DI water.

5. Determine the mass of a sample of the known metal.

6. Once the water has warmed up to a stable simmer, suspend the metal slug in it; you'll be provided with a clamp or other tool to help you do this. Let the metal simmer for at least 3 minutes and measure the temperature of the water.

- You may find the temperature reading is not completely stable, but fluctuates a little. If it does, record four consecutive temperatures. You'll average these later and use them for the boiling water temperature.

7. Immerse the lower half or so of temperature probe in the beaker full of DI water. Hold it there for a minute or more.

8. Insert the temperature probe into your calorimeter. Give the reading a minute to become reasonably stable, then start data collection by clicking on the "collect" button (green with a tan triangle). Collect temperature data for 3 minutes, then transfer the metal slug from the boiling bath to the calorimeter. Just (gently) drop the metal in, don't suspend it. Note the time you do this in number of minutes elapsed since your started data collection.

   - The water will need to be stirred a little. You can use the temperature probe to stir the water, but avoid bumping the metal and *don't let it drag on the bottom of the cup.*

9. Allow the program to continue to collect data until it stops (8-10 minutes). Stir the mixture periodically during this time (about once every 15 seconds). While you're waiting, check on your boiling water bath and add more water to it as required.

   - Note that, since you will not be able to print these data out, they must be written in your notebook. You will be destroying them in a moment, so copy the data now. You can save time by having prepared a table with the times already written in it: 0.00 min to 10.00 min in 0.25 min increments.

10. Click on the top of the time column labeled time—this should highlight all of the time data—and copy those data.

    - To copy this or anything else, press Ctrl + C, OR use the copy command from the menu bar, OR right-click the mouse and select "copy", whatever works best for you.

11. Minimize, but do not close, the Logger Pro Program. On the desktop of the computer, go into the C105 folder and open the Excel spreadsheet titled "Enthalpy of Reaction." On the spreadsheet page, click on the first cell under the heading 'time' in the "Trial 1" group and paste the data you copied a moment ago. Your time data should now occupy all the yellow cells in the columns labeled "time."

    - To paste this or anything else, press Ctrl + V, OR use the paste command from the menu bar, OR right-click the mouse and select "paste," whatever works best for you.

12. Go back to the LoggerPro program, click the top of the temperature column to highlight the temperature data, and copy those data. Go back to the Excel program and copy the temperature data into the first cell under the heading "temperature" in the "Trial 1" group.

13. Type your names in the appropriate yellow cells. Ignore the cells that ask for the concentrations of the acid and ammonia solutions, you'll use these in another experiment.

14. Empty the calorimeter reassemble it as you did previously, with more DI water in it.

15. Restore the Logger Pro program. Open the "Experiment" menu and click "Clear Latest Run."

16. Repeat the necessary procedure steps again so you have 3 total trial runs. You will paste your new data in the columns under the "Trial 2" and "Trial 3" group headings

17. Click on the tab labeled "Chart 1" (it's on the bottom left of your screen). Your data will be displayed in a temperature vs. time plot.

18. Select the "File" menu on the menu bar. Scroll down and click on "Print." On the menu that appears, put 2 in the "number of copies" window and click "OK."

19. Print the second and third charts ("Chart 2" and "Chart 3").

Part B: The Heat Capacity of an Unknown Metal Slug

20. A sign will be posed in your lab room that lists what the unknown metals available for this part could be. Note these. Choose one of the unknown metal slugs and describe it.

21. Use the same technique you used for the known metal to collect the data necessary to determine the heat capacity of your unknown metal slug.

Part C: The Density of a Known Metal Slug

22. You will need mass and volume data from your slug to determine its density. Do whatever is required to collect three sets of these data (three mass and three volume measurements). Appendix B has some information that may help you with the volume part.

    - As you collect the data you need, alternate which one, mass or volume, you are collecting. Don't take all three mass measurements at once, then all three volumes. This is done to ensure the range you ultimately calculate is representative of the technique's error limitations.

Part D: The Density of an Unknown Metal Slug

23. Use the same technique(s) you used for the known metal to collect the data necessary to determine the density of your unknown metal slug. Again, you'll need three sets.

POST LAB: CALCULATIONS

Data Plots

For each of your plots:

1. Indicate the "time of metal addition" on the x-axis.

2. Draw best-fit lines on the graph through the pre-metal-addition temperatures and the post-addition temperatures (that's two separate lines) and extrapolate them to the time of mixing. You can use the graph in the background section as an example of how to do this.

3. Indicate the temperature on each best-fit line at the "time of metal addition". Use these values used to calculate Δts for the three trials. Do the Δt calculations in your notebook, not on the graphs.

Specific Heat of Metal

4. Use your experimental data and calculated Δt values from the plots to calculate the specific heat of the known and unknown metals. The background has an example of how this can be done. Since you have three temperature data sets for both metals, you'll do this calculation three times for each.

5. Average the three specific heats you calculated for the known and the three you calculated for the unknown.

6. Calculate the standard deviation of the known's specific heats. Do the same for the unknown. Determine the range each standard deviation falls around its average.

Metal Densities

7. Use the data collected for the known and unknown metals to calculate their densities. You will do this three times for each metal (one for each data set) and have six density figures when you finish.

8. Average the metal density values for each metal and calculate their standard deviation.

9. Calculate the ranges the standard deviations you just calculated fall around their respective averages.

POST-LAB: RESULTS AND DISCUSSION

The remaining requirements for your post-lab assignment will either be provided on-line or in a handout

ENTHALPY OF FORMATION OF AMMONIUM CHLORIDE

INTRODUCTION

The experiment "Identification of a Metal" introduced you to some of the basic principles of thermodynamics and calorimetry. More specifically, you saw how the thermal energy of a piece of hot metal was transferred as heat to some water that surrounded it. By measuring the temperature increase of the water, it was possible to calculate how much energy it absorbed. This experiment will build on this concept by having you measure the transfer of energy as heat to/from a couple of chemical reactions.

In this experiment, you will measure the temperature change that results from mixing aqueous ammonium and aqueous hydrochloric acid solutions, and from dissolving solid ammonium chloride in water. This information will ultimately enable you will calculate the heat of formation of ammonium chloride from the elements nitrogen, hydrogen, and chlorine, a reaction that is not practical to measure directly.

BACKGROUND

Heat Exchanges in Reactions

As explained in the background to the "Identification of a Metal" experiment, objects, matter, etc., can exchange energy with their surroundings in the form of heat. If these things, which are given the generic term "system", gain energy as heat from their surroundings, they are said to have undergone an endothermic process. If they lose energy as heat to the surroundings, they have undergone an exothermic process.

Like the solid objects covered in the "Identification" experiment, chemical reactions can also act as systems that exchange energy as heat with their surroundings. The terminology used for these processes is similar or identical to that used for purely physical heat exchanges. Reactions/systems that "absorb" energy as heat are endothermic reactions, and those that release energy are exothermic reactions. The quantity of energy the reactions absorb or evolve, symbolized q, is a positive number for endothermic reactions and a negative number for exothermic ones.

Net transfer of energy as heat
from surroundings *to* system/reaction

Process is *endothermic*

$+q_{system}, -q_{surroundings}$

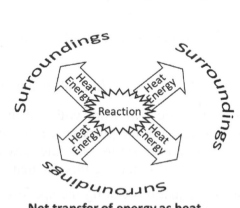

Net transfer of energy as heat
to surroundings *from* system/reaction

Process is *exothermic*

$-q_{system}, +q_{surroundings}$

The effect of an endothermic or exothermic reaction on its surroundings is the same as it is for a heat exchange in a purely physical process. When reactions absorb energy from their surroundings, the temperature of those surroundings fall. When they release energy to the surroundings, the surrounding's temperature rises. Your hand gets cold when you hold an ice cube because the ice (the system) "takes" the energy as heat from your hand (surroundings) as it melts (strictly speaking, the melting of ice is a physical process rather than a chemical one, but it illustrates the point).

In this experiment, the amount of heat released or absorbed during a chemical reaction will be studied. This will be done via calorimetry as described in the "Identification of a Metal" experiment. Although the system being studied is a reaction rather than a solid object, the principles we will use for this measurement are the same. A reaction will take place in water, which act as the reaction's surroundings. Since we can measure the temperature change this water undergoes, we can calculate how much energy as heat it gains or loses, and therefore how much energy as heat the reaction loses or gains. As for the "Identification" experiment, the reaction and its surroundings will take place in an insulated vessel, a calorimeter, to isolate them from the air, benchtop, etc. of the lab room.

Calorimetry Calculations

The calculations performed to determine the energy as heat gained or lost by a chemical reaction are very similar to the ones used to determine the specific heat of a metal. Nevertheless, the following example should help you in case the differences between them cause you any problems.

Let's say a chemical reaction is initiated in a calorimeter that contains 75.2 mL of water. The water is at an initial temperature of 22.7°C, and rises to a final temperature of 78.4°C.

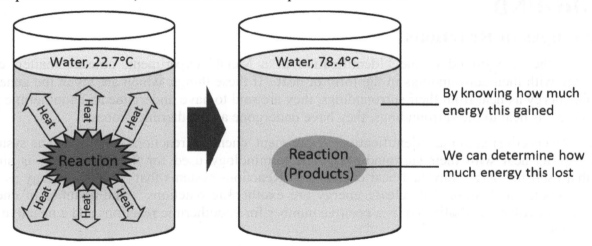

Since the quantity of water used is in mL but the equation requires it to be in grams, we will have to convert 75.2 mL to g:

$$75.2 \; \text{mL water} \; \times \; 1.00\frac{\text{g}}{\text{mL}} \; = 75.2 \; \text{g water}$$

Some of the reactants you will work with will be provided in solutions, and these solutions will essentially provide their own water. For the purposes of this experiment, you can just use the density of water (1.00 g/mL) and the volume of solution used to calculate how much water surrounds your reacting molecules. Ignore the presence of any solutes when making this calculation.

We can now use the equation relating the specific heat, initial temperature, final temperature, and mass of the water to determine how much energy as heat the water absorbed. In its general form, this equation is:

$$q = c \times m \times (t_{final} - t_{initial})$$

Plugging the various pieces of information we have so far into this equation, including the specific heat of water (4.18 J/g·°C), it becomes:

$$q_{water} = 4.18 \; \text{J/g·°C} \; \times \; 75.2 \; \text{g} \; \times \; (78.4°C - 22.7°C)$$

Solving for q:

$$q_{water} = 17500 \text{ J} \quad \text{OR} \quad 17.5 \text{ kJ}$$

As for the "Identification" experiment, since all of the energy absorbed by the water (q_{water}) evolved from the reaction, the value of q for the reaction (q_{rxn}) will be equal in magnitude but opposite in sign to q_{water}:

$$q_{water} = -q_{rxn}$$

Since q_{water} was 17.5 kJ, q_{rxn} is -17.5 J.

Reaction Signs

You will note that q_{water} calculated as a positive number and q_{rxn} a negative number. This makes sense because the temperature of the water increased in this example, indicating a net transfer of energy as heat from the reaction to the water. From this information, we know that the reaction must have been exothermic, and this is confirmed by the negative sign of q for q_{rxn}. A decrease in the water's temperature would have indicated an endothermic reaction, and q_{rxn} would—or should—have calculated as a positive number.

Measurement of Temperature Changes

The temperature measurements you take in this experiment will be done in the same way they were taken in the "Identification" experiment. Briefly, you will plot temperature and time data, extrapolate a best fit line through the "before reaction" data, extrapolate a second best-fit line through the "after mixing" data, and use these lines to determine the change in water temperature at the time the reaction is initiated. For a full description and example of this, see the "Identification of a Metal" background.

Heat and Enthalpy of a Reaction

Knowing how much energy as heat that flows from or to a reaction is useful, but does have limitations. For one, it tells us nothing regarding what the overall energy "content" of the reactants and products are. As you will learn later on this in course, this information can be used to help us predict whether or not a reaction will occur, and/or how much energy might be required to make a reaction occur. For this reason, the change in energy reactants undergo as they become products is generally not reported as a quantity of heat, but as another, related property: the change in the reaction system's enthalpy.

Enthalpy, denoted "H", is like energy in general in that it is a somewhat nebulous concept. However, it can generally be thought of as the "thermal energy," or "heat content," of a reaction system. The enthalpy of a system can fall and rise as that system undergoes exothermic and endothermic processes respectively:

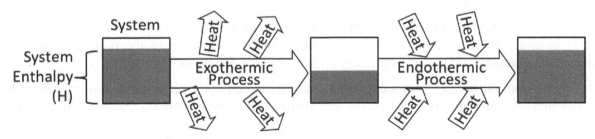

Although enthalpy and heat are related, though they are not synonymous. Heat is a transfer of thermal energy—a kind of energy related to the kinetic energy of molecules—from one system or object to another. Enthalpy, a state function, is one component of a system's total internal energy. The change in a system's enthalpy will be equal to its heat flux, but only under conditions of constant pressure.

$$\Delta H = q_{rxn} \text{ (at constant pressure)}$$

Constant pressure basically means the reaction is not constricted by a rigid, closed container. Any reaction you perform in the open air—including those in your coffee cup calorimeter—are constant pressure reactions.

Enthalpy and Equations

The specific value reported for the ΔH of a reaction is typically associated with a balanced chemical equation for that reaction. In doing this, the value of ΔH will be given per the number of moles of reactant or product indicated in the reaction's stoichiometry coefficients. For example, ΔH for the reaction

$$2 H_2(g) + O_2(g) \longrightarrow 2 H_2O(l)$$

is -571.66 kJ as currently written, i.e., its enthalpy change is -573.66 kJ per 1 mole of O_2 and 2 moles of H_2. However, if the coefficients in a reaction equation are multiplied or divided to yield a different set of coefficients, the value of ΔH for the reaction will also change. Consider what happens if we divide the coefficients in the above reaction by 2 to provide the following:

$$H_2(g) + \tfrac{1}{2} O_2(g) \longrightarrow H_2O(l)$$

The enthalpy change for the reaction when written this way—per one mole H_2 and 0.5 mole O_2—is -285.83 kJ.

Although ΔH has units of J/mol for some very specific types of reactions (see the next page), it generally has units of just J (or kJ); its magnitude therefore depends on how the balanced chemical equation is written. Remember, enthalpy is an extensive property, dependent on the amount of material that reacts.

Enthalpy of Reaction Terminology

There are a few phrases that you need to be familiar with when working with systems that undergo enthalpy changes. The **enthalpy of reaction** is a generic term used for any type of reaction undergoes an enthalpy change. The following terms are used for specific types of reactions:

The **Enthalpy of Neutralization** (ΔH_{neut}) refers to the enthalpy of reaction for an acid/base neutralization reaction. You will measure such a reaction in this experiment.

Enthalpy of Solution (ΔH_{sol}), the enthalpy change when one mole of a substance is dissolved in water, is another type of enthalpy you will measure in this experiment.

Enthalpy of Formation describes the enthalpy of the formation of one mole of a compound from the elements that comprise it in standard state conditions (most stable physical state at a pressure of 1 bar at the specified temperature). For example, the equation for the enthalpy of formation of methanol, CH_3OH, would be given as:

$$C(s) + 2 H_2(g) + \tfrac{1}{2} O_2(g) \longrightarrow CH_3OH(l) \qquad \Delta H = -238.7 \text{ kJ}$$

Note that the reactants in this equation are expressed in the form they would exist in given standard state conditions; e.g., $H_2(g)$ instead of $H_2(l)$ or $H^+(aq)$. Consult your text book if you are unsure what form any given compound is in under standard conditions. Also note that the coefficient of the product is set to one and the coefficients of the reactants are set appropriately so the equation balances.

Enthalpy of formation values have been experimentally tabulated for a huge number of compounds and can be utilized to calculate the enthalpy of reaction for any arbitrary reaction involving these compounds by using:

$$\Delta H_{rxn} = \sum(n\Delta H_f)\text{products} - \sum(n\Delta H_f)\text{reactants}$$

where n represents the stoichiometric coefficients for individual reactants and products. If you look at one of these tables, you may notice that most of them do not list ΔH_f values for elements. This is because, by definition, the ΔH_f values of elements in their standard states are exactly zero.

Hess's Law

The formation of any given compound(s) from reactants can proceed as a single step involving one reaction or as several steps involving several reactions. For example, glucose can be eaten and catabolized into carbon dioxide and water in a series of reactions in the cells of an organism (in the glycolysis and tri-carboxylic acid cycles, as you may recall from a biology course), or it can simply be lit on fire and burned. In both cases the over-all reaction is:

$$C_6H_{12}O_6(s) + 6O_2(g) \rightarrow 6CO_2(g) + 6H_2O(l)$$

Although the reactions that the glucose and oxygen take in getting to carbon dioxide and water are different in these two cases, the change in enthalpy for the over-all reaction, its ΔH_{rxn} value, is the same. This phenomenon, which is true of any combination of reactants and products, is described by Hess's law. Hess's law states that ΔH_{rxn} is only dependent upon the initial reactants and the final products in a reaction; it is independent of the steps involved in getting from reactants to products. This is particularly useful when the ΔH_{rxn} for a reaction of interest is not known, but there are other reactions for which the ΔH's are known and that can be added together to give the reaction of interest. This makes it possible to calculate ΔH's that would be difficult to measure in lab. For example, in this lab you will be using hydrochloric acid in its familiar aqueous state, but there is no enthalpy of formation for aqueous hydrochloric acid.

$$\frac{1}{2} H_2(g) + \frac{1}{2} Cl_2(g) \rightarrow HCl(aq) \qquad \Delta H_{rxn} = ?$$

However, both the enthalpy of formation for hydrochloric acid in the gas state and for dissolving the gas in water are known. Hess's Law states that this information can be used to find the ΔH_{rxn} of interest. This is done by adding together the two reactions for which we know the enthalpy of and their associated enthalpy values

$$\frac{1}{2} H_2(g) + \frac{1}{2} Cl_2(g) \rightarrow \cancel{HCl(g)} \qquad \Delta H_f = -92.3 \text{ kJ/mole}$$

$$+ \quad \cancel{HCl(g)} \rightarrow HCl(aq) \qquad \Delta H = -75.1 \text{ kJ/mole}$$

$$\frac{1}{2} H_2(g) + \frac{1}{2} Cl_2(g) \rightarrow HCl(aq) \qquad \Delta H_{rxn} = -167.4 \text{ kJ/mole}$$

Your ultimate objective in this experiment is to determine the enthalpy of formation for solid ammonium chloride salt. Because it is difficult, nigh impossible, to measure the formation of ammonium chloride when starting from its constituent elements, you will use Hess's Law and the enthalpy of formation/reaction values of other compounds and reactions to calculate it.

In this lab you will experimentally determine ΔH's for two processes: (1) the reaction of aqueous ammonia with hydrochloric acid and (2) the dissolving of ammonium chloride salt in water. These represent two of the ΔH values that you will require to calculate the enthalpy of ammonium chloride formation. In addition to these, there are a few others you will need for this calculation.

Reaction	Enthalpy of Reaction
$\frac{1}{2} N_2(g) + 1\frac{1}{2} H_2(g) \rightarrow NH_3(g)$	$\Delta H_f = -45.8$ kJ
$\frac{1}{2} H_2(g) + \frac{1}{2} Cl_2(g) \rightarrow HCl(g)$	$\Delta H_f = -92.3$ kJ
$NH_3(g) \rightarrow NH_3(aq)$	$\Delta H = -35.4$ kJ
$HCl(g) \rightarrow HCl(aq)$	$\Delta H = -75.1$ kJ

See the Laboratory Report Guidelines for a description of the Data Plot guidelines and requirements for this course.

PROCEDURE CITATION

Begin your data and observations section for this experiment with a citation for the procedure you will follow.

Properly cite the procedure from your laboratory manual. Be sure to leave room to note any adjustments you make to the procedure.

PROCEDURE

This experiment will involve the collection of temperature readings at specific time intervals. The program you will use to do this is setup to record 40 temperature readings over 10 minutes; leave enough room to record these in your manual for each part of the experiment.

As you perform this experiment, make a note of all the equipment and chemicals you use. Make a sketch of your calorimeter and neatly label it.

Part A: Set Up

1. Set up the Styrofoam cup calorimeter as shown in the figure below. Make sure that the temperature probe does not touch the stirrer, or the bottom or sides of the cup

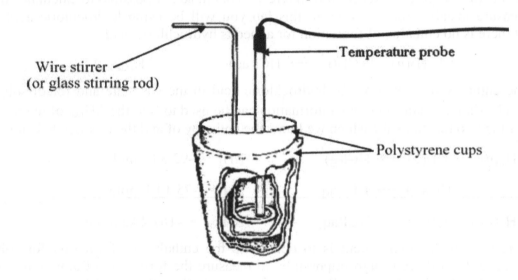

2. Open the "Heat of Reaction" Logger Pro program in the C105 folder. A pop-up window may appear titled "Sensor Confirmation." Select "Connect" if it does.

    *   If the program and probe are working correctly, a temperature reading of somewhere between 19°C and 26°C will be indicated in the bottom left of your screen. If not, tell your TA.

Part B: Heat of Neutralization

3. Use a graduated cylinder to measure out 50 mL of hydrochloric acid and pour it into the Styrofoam cup calorimeter. Ensure that the bottom of the temperature probe is immersed in this solution.

    *   Note: 50 mL is only guideline; the actual amount you add will differ. The rules for properly reading the meniscus on your glassware also apply.

4. Wait several minutes for the temperature to equilibrate.

5. Thoroughly wash your graduated cylinder and rinse it with a few milliliters of ammonia solution.

6. Measure 50 mL of the ammonia solution in a graduated cylinder, but do not add it to the calorimeter.

7. Start data collection by clicking on the "collect" button (green with a tan triangle). The moment you start collecting is time = 0 min.

8. Collect temperature data for 3 minutes. The program should record a data point every 15 seconds (if not, tell your TA).

9. Quickly pour the ammonia solution into the calorimeter and note the time you did this. Stir the reaction thoroughly, being careful not to let the stirring rod drag on the bottom of the calorimeter cup.

10. Allow the program to continue to collect data until it stops (10 minutes). Stir the mixture periodically during this time (about once every 15 seconds).

   - Note that, since you will not be able to print these data out, they must be written in your notebook. You will be destroying them in a moment, so copy the data now. You can save time by having prepared a table with the times already written in it: 0.00 min to 10.00 min in 0.25 min increments.

11. Click on the top of the time column labeled time—this should highlight all of the time data—and copy those data.

   - To copy this or anything else, press Ctrl + C, OR use the copy command from the menu bar, OR right-click the mouse and select "copy", whatever works best for you.

12. Minimize, but do not close, the Logger Pro Program. On the desktop of the computer, go into the C105 folder and open the Excel spreadsheet titled "Enthalpy of Reaction." On the spreadsheet page, click on the first cell under the heading 'time' in the "Trial 1" group and paste the data you copied a moment ago. Your time data should now occupy all the yellow cells in the columns labeled "time."

   - To paste this or anything else, press Ctrl + V, OR use the paste command from the menu bar, OR right-click the mouse and select "paste," whatever works best for you.

13. Go back to the LoggerPro program, click the top of the temperature column to highlight the temperature data, and copy those data. Go back to the Excel program and copy the temperature data into the first cell under the heading "temperature" in the "Trial 1" group.

14. Type your names and the concentrations of the acid and ammonia solutions in the appropriate yellow cells.

15. Empty and rinse the calorimeter, rinse your graduated cylinders, and reassemble the calorimeter as you did in the set up.

16. Restore the Logger Pro program. Open the "Experiment" menu and click "Clear Latest Run."

17. Repeat the necessary procedure steps again so you have 2 total trial runs (this is everything after the Setup section). You will paste your new data in the columns under the "Trial 2" group heading

18. Click on the tab labeled "Chart 1" (it's on the bottom left of your screen). Your data will be displayed in a temperature vs. time plot.

19. Select the "File" menu on the menu bar. Scroll down and click on "Print." On the menu that appears, put 2 in the "number of copies" window and click "OK." Be certain both partners have a copy of this plot before proceeding.

20. Click on the tab labeled "Chart 2" and again print.

Part C: Heat of Solution

21. Clean your calorimeter and rinse with DI water. Reassemble it as in part A.

22. Measure 100 mL of DI water into your calorimeter cup.

23. Fill a clean weighing bottle to the same level of NH_4Cl as the example provided by your instructor. Weigh the bottle to determine its mass.

   - Note: it is permissible to take a little more or a little less than what is displayed by the example. This will be accounted for in your calculations.

24. Restore the Logger Pro Program. Open the "Experiment" menu and click "Clear Latest Run."

25. Start data collection by clicking on the "collect" button. The moment you start collecting is time = 0 min.

26. Collect temperature data for 3 minutes.

27. Quickly add all of the solid NH_4Cl from your weighing bottle to the calorimeter and stir until the solid has completely dissolved. Note the time you do this in your notebook. After the solid has dissolved, periodically stir at a slow pace and be careful not to let the stirring rod drag on the bottom of the calorimeter cup.

- Let the program record time and temperature data until it stops.

28. After the program stops, re-weigh the weighing bottle and calculate how much NH_4Cl you added.

29. Click on the data table window. On the menu bar, select the "Edit" menu. Scroll down and click on "Select All." Your name and temperature data should now be highlighted. Again select the "Edit" menu and click "Copy."

30. Minimize (but do not close) the Logger Pro Program. On the Excel spreadsheet page, click on the first cell under the heading 'time' in the "Trial 3 group," blue colored section. On the menu bar, select the "Edit" menu. Scroll down and click on "Paste". Your data should now occupy all the blue cells in the columns labeled 'time' and 'temperature' in the "Trial 3" group.

31. Fill in the appropriate blue cells with your names and the concentration of the NH_4Cl solution.

32. Restore the Logger Pro program. Open the "Experiment" menu and click "Clear Latest Run."

33. Repeat the necessary part C procedure steps again so you have two total trial runs. You will paste your new data in the columns under the "Trial 4" group heading

34. Click on the tab labeled "Chart 3" (bottom left of your screen). Print two copies of this. After both copies are finished printing, open "Chart 4" and again print two copies.

35. Close both the Excel and the Logger Pro programs. When they ask if you wish to save, select "No."

36. You must have all plots signed by your TA before leaving lab.

Part D: Clean-up

37. Deposit all remaining solutions and solid ammonium chloride in the lab's waste container.

38. Wash all glassware with detergent, rinse thoroughly with water, and place on your towel to dry.

39. Thoroughly rinse the Styrofoam cup and leave upside down to dry.

40. Clean-up all spills and throw all garbage in the garbage cans.

POST-LAB: CALCULATIONS

Data Plots

For each of your plots:

1. Indicate the "time of mixing" on the x-axis.

2. Draw best-fit lines on the graph through the pre-mixing temperatures and the post-mixing temperatures (that's two separate lines) and extrapolate them to the time of mixing. You can use the graph in the background to the "Identification of a Metal" experiment as an example of how to do this.

3. Indicate the temperature on each best-fit line at the time of mixing. Use these values used to calculate Δts for your reaction trials. Do the Δt calculations in your notebook, not on the graphs.

Heat Calculations

4. For each of your data sets, calculate:

- the mass of the water in your calorimeter (The presence of HCl, NH_3 and/or NH_4Cl will add a small amount of mass to your solutions, but you can ignore this; just consider the water)

- ΔT from your graphs

- the amount of heat absorbed or lost by the solution (q_{soln}) and reaction (q_{rxn})

- the number of moles of ammonium chloride created or used

- ΔH for the reaction in kilojoules per mole of ammonium chloride

5. Average the two ΔH you calculated for the neutralization of ammonia with HCl and calculate their standard deviation.

6. Average the two ΔH you calculated for the solution of ammonium chloride and calculate their standard deviation.

Enthalpy of Formation

7. Use the information given in the background, the ΔH values you just calculated, and Hess's Law to calculate ΔH for the following:

   a. $NH_3(g) + HCl(g) \rightarrow NH_4Cl(s)$. You will need four total reactions, and their associated ΔH values, to do this. Two of these four ΔH values are the averages you calculated in the previous steps

   b. The heat of formation of $NH_4Cl(s)$. You will need the values you just calculated and those of 2 more reactions to do this.

POST-LAB: RESULTS AND DISCUSSION

The remaining requirements for your post-lab assignment will either be provided on-line or in a handout.

THE DENSITY OF AIR

INTRODUCTION

Wood floats on water because it is less dense than water, while iron, being more dense than water, sinks. Therefore, you can conclude that the density of water is somewhere between that of wood and iron. For other substances, however, it is much more difficult to draw similar conclusions from simple observations. For example, is argon gas more or less dense than xenon gas? Their relative densities cannot be determined in the same way those for wood, water, and iron were because gases are colorless and we are not able to see whether or not one is "floating" on the other. However, the Ideal Gas Law can be used to answer this question by a simple calculation.

Using the Ideal Gas Law, it can be shown that two different samples of gas that both contain the same number of gas molecules will occupy the same volume provided the temperature and pressure of those samples are the same. Therefore, if a number of xenon molecules and a like number of argon molecules are both collected at the same temperature and pressure, they will occupy the same volume. Also, because these two samples contain the same number of molecules, and because xenon is a heavier element than argon, the mass of the xenon sample will be greater than the mass of the argon sample. Therefore, because the xenon sample has a greater mass for the same volume, it could be concluded that xenon gas is denser than argon gas.

Your objective in this experiment is to determine the density of air. As you may recall from the experiment "Laboratory Techniques and Measurements", this will require you to calculate two things: the volume of a sample of air, and the mass of that sample.

BACKGROUND

Air is a mixture of gasses that consists primarily of nitrogen and oxygen with trace amounts (~1-2%) of argon, water vapor, and other gasses. Of all the gasses present in air, the relative amounts of nitrogen, oxygen, and argon tend to remain relatively constant from place to place, but the amount of water vapor varies depending on location and other factors.

The density of air, like that of all gasses, is affected by a number of factors, including its temperature, elevation, and the quantity of water vapor in it. Because the density of water vapor is less than that of nitrogen or oxygen, a sample of air with a high water vapor content will be less dense than an otherwise equivalent sample of dry air. Samples of air that are relatively warm or at a high elevation will also be less dense than those that are cooler or at a lower elevation. You may notice that increases in temperature, altitude, and water vapor all affect air density the same way: they lower it. A memory aid aviators use to remember this is that air is less dense in places that are "hot, high, and humid."

Calculating the Density of Air

In order to calculate the density of a sample of air (or any substance), both the mass and volume of that sample must be determined. Determining the sample's volume is fairly simple because air, like any type of gas, will completely fill the container it is in; the volume of the sample is therefore equal to the total volume of its container. An Erlenmeyer flask will serve as your sample container in this experiment, so the volume of your sample will be equal to the volume of your flask.

Although measuring the volume of air in an Erlenmeyer flask is a relatively straightforward process, determining the mass of the air in that flask is a little more complicated. Since the air cannot be removed from the flask and placed directly on a scale, it will be necessary to measure the combined mass of both the flask and the air inside it. The mass of the air in that flask can be then calculated by subtracting the mass of the flask itself—this being its mass with nothing at all inside, not even air—from the mass of a flask with air:

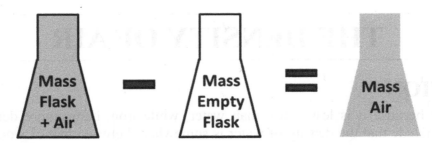

Naturally, in order to make this calculation we would first have to measure the mass of a truly empty flask. However, it is not possible to do this by weighing the flask because a perfect vacuum would have to be created in it beforehand, which is difficult to accomplish. We therefore need some way to determine the flask's mass indirectly; one that does not involve evacuating it first.

One way to indirectly determine the mass of the flask is to fill it with a substance such as a gas of known composition, and therefore known density and mass, and subtract the mass of this gas from the mass of the flask + gas:

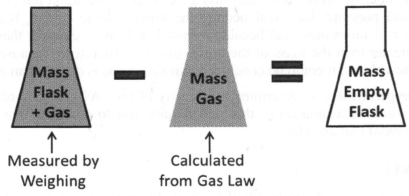

In this experiment, the gas of known composition you will fill the flask with will be carbon dioxide, which will be supplied as dry ice (solid CO_2). When a piece of dry ice is placed in the flask, it will sublime and fill the flask with CO_2 gas.

Ideal Gas Law

As for the air we are ultimately trying to determine the mass of, it will not be possible to remove the gaseous CO_2 from the flask and measure its mass separately. However, it is possible to use the Ideal Gas Law to calculate its mass instead.

The Ideal Gas Law is:

$$PV = nRT$$

P = pressure in atmospheres

V = volume in liters

n = number of moles

R = 0.0820575 L atm/mol K

T = temperature in Kelvin

Note that this equation requires pressure to be in atmospheres and temperature to be in Kelvin. Since these are more commonly reported in mm Hg and degrees Celsius, however, they will first need to be converted. Use the following conversion factors to do this:

1 atmosphere = 760 torr = 760 mm Hg   T in Kelvin = °C + 273.15

Calculations

Moles and Mass of CO_2

Over the course of the experiment you are about to perform, you will collect flask volume and temperature data and be given the pressure of your lab room. From these three pieces of information, it is possible to calculate the number of moles, and ultimately the mass, of CO_2 in the flask. This can be done as follows.

Let's say you are given a flask with a volume of 549.2 mL that is at a temperature of 28.9° Celsius and the pressure of the room is 679.8 Torr. Before we can apply the gas law, it is first necessary to convert these numbers into liters, Kelvin, and atmospheres respectively. If you do this for yourself, you will arrive at 0.5492 L, 302.1 K, and 0.8945 atmospheres. The gas law equation then becomes:

$$0.8945 \text{ atm x } 0.5492 \text{ L} = n \text{ x } 0.0820575 \ \frac{\text{L·atm}}{\text{mol·K}} \text{ x } 302.1 \text{ K}$$

If you solve for n, you will find that a flask of this volume and at this temperature and pressure holds 1.982×10^{-2} moles of gas. Note that this number can stand for the total number of moles of any gas in the flask, not just CO_2.

Once the number of moles of CO_2 in the flask is known, we can calculate the mass of it present from the molar mass of CO_2:

$$1.982 \times 10^{-2} \text{ mol x } \frac{44.01 \text{ g}}{1 \text{ mol}} = 0.8722 \text{ grams } CO_2$$

Mass of Air

Now that we know the number of grams of CO_2 in the flask, we can come back to the original problem of determining the mass of air in it when it is filled with air instead. Let's say the flask weighs 124.151 grams when it is filled with CO_2 and 123.858 grams when filled with air. Since we know that 0.8722 grams of its filled-with-CO_2 mass comes from the CO_2 itself, the mass of the empty flask must be 123.279 grams (124.151 g – 0.8722 g). Therefore, the mass of the air inside it is 0.5790 grams (123.858 g –123.279 g).

Density of Air

As was stated in the background to the "Laboratory Techniques" experiment, the density of any substance can be found by dividing its mass by its volume. Our sample of air has a mass of 0.5790 grams and occupies a volume of 0.5492 liters, so its density is 1.054 grams/L.

$$D = \frac{M}{V}$$

PROCEDURE CITATION

Begin your data and observations section for this experiment with a citation for the procedure you will follow.

PROCEDURE

As you perform this experiment, make a note of all the equipment and chemicals you use. Be sure to include the balance number when you do this. Each trial you perform will include the mass of the flask filled with air and the mass of flask filled with CO_2. In addition you will be recording temperature, atmospheric pressure, and the volume of your flask.

1. Check that your flask will fit into the top loading balance with the cover of the balance closed. If your flask is too heavy or too tall for the balance, you will receive an error message on the balance display.

2. Cover your flask with a piece of aluminum foil large enough to completely cover the top and extend down the neck about 2 cm.

3. Poke a very small hole in the center of the foil with a pin. The top of the foil should be flat; make sure it is not pushed into the flask or bubbled above the rim.

4. Have your lab instructor place a piece of dry ice (solid CO_2) into your flask and re-cover it with the same piece of aluminum foil.

> **Caution: Dry ice can cause severe frostbite. Do not touch it!**

5. Wait until all of the dry ice has sublimed. Once it has, let the flask warm to room temperature and measure its mass. This is the mass of the flask filled with CO_2.

   - If there is liquid visible at the bottom of the flask when all the CO_2 has sublimed, remove the foil, turn the flask over and wave your hand below the flask to empty the CO_2 out of it. Make sure the flask is dry, then begin a new trial with a new piece of dry ice.

6. Remove the foil, invert the flask, and wave your hand below it to fill it with air. Re-cap the flask with the foil and take the mass of the flask and foil. This is the mass of the flask with air in it.

7. Use your thermometer to measure room temperature. 20.2400

8. Repeat the air/CO_2 mass and temperature measurements two more times, so you have a total of 3 sets of data.

9. Go into the 105 folder on your computer and open the Excel program titled "Density of Air". Enter your mass data into this program.

10. Check your standard deviation. If it is 0.01 grams or less, proceed. Otherwise, collect three more sets of mass data.

    - If your standard deviation is more than 0.01 grams, you may have moisture condensation on your flask.

11. Fill the flask to the brim with tap water. Pour all of the water into a graduated cylinder and measure the volume to the appropriate number of significant figures.

12. Rinse the inside of your flask with methanol and set it upside-down on a towel to dry. Pour the excess methanol in the lab's waste container.

13. Note the room's pressure. This will be written on the board for you.

Clean-up

14. Make sure all scrap foil and garbage are in the trash can.

15. Leave your equipment clean and laid out on the towel for the next class.

POST-LAB: CALCULATIONS

1. Use your flask volume, temperature, and pressure data to calculate the mass of gaseous carbon dioxide your flask held.

2. Use your "flask + CO_2" and "flask + air" mass data to calculate the density of the air in your lab room. Do this three times, using data from each of your three trials.

3. Average the air density values you just calculated.

4. Calculate the standard deviation of the three density figures.

5. Calculate the range the standard deviation you just calculated falls around the average. Do this by subtracting one standard deviation from the average and adding one to the average.

POST-LAB: RESULTS AND DISCUSSION

The remaining requirements for your post-lab assignment will either be provided on-line or in a handout.

1) CO_2 78.680
   Air   72.110

2) CO_2 78.672
   Air   72.113

3) CO_2 78.687
   Air

$CO_2 \to .2486$

$$D = \frac{M}{V}$$

$$\sqrt{\frac{(1.08-1.25)^2 + (1.35-1.25)^2 + (1.33-1.25)^2}{3-1}}$$

THE SHAPES OF MOLECULES AND IONS

INTRODUCTION

Most of the chemical compounds you have encountered in your studies of chemistry have so-far been depicted as a formula, such as H_2O for water and Na_2CO_3 for sodium carbonate. Although these formulas are useful, as they indicate what types of atoms/elements are in a compound and in what proportions, they only provide limited information regarding how those atoms are arranged with respect to each other. For instance, are the hydrogens in a water molecule attached to opposite sides of the oxygen atom, are they close to each other on one side, or do they lie something in between? This information is important as it can provide insights into the physical properties of a compound.

As you may have guessed, the atoms that makeup molecules are bonded to each other in specific orientations that vary from compound to compound. These arrangements are often referred to as the shape or geometry of a molecule. In this experiment, you will learn what these orientations are and how to deduce them for any specific molecule. You will also learn two ways of depicting the geometry of a molecule: by making physical, three-dimensional models, and drawing the molecules on a two-dimensional surface (i.e., a piece of paper or a computer screen).

BACKGROUND

Lewis Structures

Understanding a molecule's geometry begins with knowing what types of bonds it has and how many lone-pairs of electrons it contains. This information is provided by the molecule's Lewis structure. These structures, sometimes called "dot diagrams", consist of chemical symbols for the elements in a molecule, lines for the bonds, and a dot for each valence electron.

Briefly, to draw a Lewis structure for a molecule:

1. Count up the total number of valence electrons around all the atoms in the molecule or ion. This number corresponds to the column number of the elements in the periodic table. Water, for instance, contains six valence electrons contributed by oxygen and another two from the two hydrogen atoms for a total of eight valence electrons:

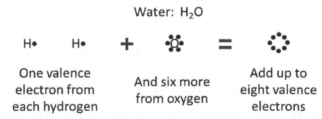

2. Draw single bonds between the central atom and the other atoms. Each of the hydrogen atoms in a water molecule will be joined to the central oxygen atom by a single bond, for a total of two bonds in the molecule as a whole.

3. Assign pairs of electrons, also called lone pairs, to the non-hydrogen atoms in the molecule so that each atom except hydrogen is associated with a total of eight electrons. The electrons in each bond directly attached to any given atom count toward this eight-electron quota. The total number of electrons in all the molecule's bonds and lone pairs cannot exceed the number tallied in the first step. If you "run out" of

valence electrons before each atom has 8 electrons, assign a double bond between two of the atoms and repeat this step.

The electrons in the two oxygen-to-hydrogen bonds in a water molecule provide that molecule's oxygen atom with four electrons. The oxygen's quota of eight electrons can therefore be fulfilled by adding an additional four electrons in the form of two lone pairs.

Lewis structure for water

Four electrons in two lone pairs and another four in the O-H bonds add up to eight electrons associated with the oxygen atom

Note that the oxygen atom in water has eight electrons and each hydrogen atom has two electrons. There are a few exceptions to the eight-electron rule besides hydrogen. Boron, for example, only requires a total of six.

The rule that most atoms require a total of eight electrons around them is sometimes called the octet rule.

AXE Classes

After determining the Lewis structure for a molecule, the next step in determining its geometry is to assign an AX_mE_n class to its central atom. The "A" represents the central atom, the m in X_m represents the number of bonded atoms, also called bonding groups, attached to the central atom, and the n in E_n is the number of lone pairs of electrons around the central atom. The bonded atoms (ms) and lone electron pairs (ns) are collectively referred to as electron groups. Since water contains two bonding groups and two lone pairs of electrons, for a total of four electron groups, it belongs to the AX_2E_2 class.

A = the molecule's central atom

X = the number of bonding groups attached to the central atom

E = the number of lone electron pairs associated with the central atom

X + E = the number of electron groups around the central atom

The distinction between the number of bonding groups and the number of electron groups a molecule contains is an important one because it will ultimately give rise to two distinct, but related, molecule geometries: the geometry of the electron groups, and that of the bonding groups only. The former is referred to as a molecule's electron geometry and the latter its molecular geometry.

Electron Geometry

The electron geometry of any given molecule can be predicted by one basic rule: the electron groups around a central atom will arrange themselves so they are as far apart from each other as possible while still attached to the central atom. This rule is more properly called the Valence Shell Electron Pair Repulsion (VSEPR) theory.

Carbon dioxide provides a relatively simple example of VSEPR theory. The carbon atom in CO_2 is associated with two bonding groups (the oxygen atoms) and no lone pairs of electrons, so its AXE class is AX_2E_0. VSEPR theory predicts these two groups will arrange themselves so they are on opposite sides of the central carbon atom, which is the furthest they can be from each other and still be attached to the carbon. This arrangement, with all three atoms in a straight line, is called a linear geometry. Other geometries that correspond to three, four, and more electron groups are as follows:

Electron Groups	Geometry
Two	Linear
Three	Trigonal Planar
Four	Tetrahedral

Electron Groups	Geometry
Five	Trigonal Bipyramidal
Six	Octahedral

You may have noticed the double bonds in carbon dioxide do not affect its AXE classification or electron geometry. This is true of any molecule that contains double or triple bonds; the two pairs of electrons in a double bond and the three pairs of electrons in a triple bond count as just one electron group.

Water is a common molecule with a tetrahedral electron geometry; that is, a pyramid with a triangular base. Its AXE class is AX_2E_2, so it has four total electron groups. Note how the four groups arrange themselves so their positions correspond to the four points of a tetrahedron.

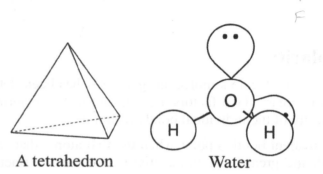

A tetrahedron   Water

Bond Angles

The bond angles associated with the above geometries are as follows. The model kits you will use in this experiment have pieces with these fixed angles.

Electron Pair Geometry	Bond Angles
Linear	180°
Trigonal planar	120°
Tetrahedral	109.5°
Trigonal bipyramidal	90°, 120°, 180°
Octahedral	90°, 180°

Molecular Geometry/Molecular Shape*

Once the electron geometry of an atom is known, the geometry of the bonding groups (bonded atoms) can be determined. This type of geometric classification, molecular geometry, is similar to electron geometry, but whereas electron geometry describes the orientation of *all* the electron groups around a central atom, molecular geometry describes the orientation of the *bonding groups* only. If a molecule has no unshared pairs of electrons, its molecular geometry will be the same as its electron geometry. Otherwise, they will be different.

*Molecular geometry is sometimes referred to as molecular shape, though the phrase "molecular geometry" is more common.

Except for molecules with a linear electron geometry, each type of electron geometry has two or more different possible molecular geometries associated with it. Four of the more common ones you will encounter include trigonal planar, bent, tetrahedral, and trigonal pyramidal. Your textbook has a complete listing of all the molecular geometries you are expected to know for this course.

Water, AX_2E_2, and sulfur dioxide, AX_2E_1, provide good examples of molecules with a bent molecular geometry. Note how the central atoms and bonding groups form a "V" shape in both molecules:

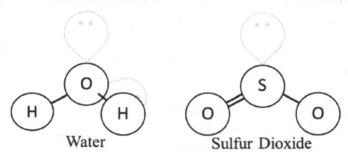

Water   Sulfur Dioxide

Polarity

Once a molecule's molecular geometry has been determined, it is possible to predict whether that molecule or ion is polar. Two factors are relevant to this determination: the molecular geometry of the molecule, and the polarity of the individual bonds within it.

A covalent bond is polar when the two atoms that share the bond have different electronegativities. The atom with the greater electronegativity will have a fractional negative charge, while the other atom will have a fractional positive charge; these are indicated by a "δ^-" and "δ^+" sign respectively. For instance, consider oxygen, with an electronegativity of 3.5, and hydrogen, with an electronegativity of 2.1. Since oxygen has a greater electronegativity, it will tend to "pull" the electrons in an oxygen-hydrogen bond toward it. Thus, the density of electrons in the bond will be higher closer to the oxygen than the hydrogen, resulting in a slight negative charge over the oxygen and a positive charge over the hydrogen.

Hydrogen will carry a fractional positive charge in an oxygen-to-hydrogen bond and oxygen a fractional negative charge. Shading indicates relative electron density. The arrow points to the "negative" pole.

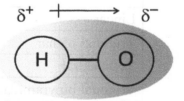

The geometry of a molecule with polar bonds will determine whether or not that molecule will have an overall polarity. The geometry of a water molecule is such that it can be divided into two regions, with the hydrogen atoms in one region and the oxygen atom in the other. Because the individual bonds in a water molecule are polar, with the oxygen atom having a fractional negative charge, the "oxygen region" of the molecule will also carry a fractional negative charge. Conversely, the "hydrogen region" will carry a fractional positive charge. This results in the overall molecule having a dipole and therefore being polar.

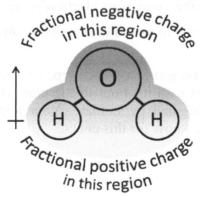

The effect of a molecule's geometry on its overall polarity can be further highlighted if we compare the polarity of water with that of carbon dioxide. Similar to water, the individual bonds in a carbon dioxide molecule are polar because of the difference in electronegativity between carbon and oxygen. Unlike water, however, the bonding groups in a carbon dioxide molecule are arranged on opposite sides of the central carbon atom, which gives the molecule a linear—and symmetrical—geometry. Because the "pull" the electrons undergo is symmetrical, it is not possible to identify one side that carries a fractional charge unique to that side. The molecule is therefore non-polar.

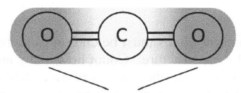

Symmetrical fractional charges in CO_2
directly oppose each other and cancel out

From our comparison of these two molecules we can derive two basic rules regarding the polarity of molecules:

1. If the molecule has polar bonds and it is possible to identify one side of it that carries a fractional negative or positive charge, then the molecule will be polar.

2. If the molecule has polar bonds, but it is not possible to identify one side that carries a fractional charge unique to that side, then the molecule will be non-polar.

Three-Dimensional Drawings

Since many of the molecules you will encounter in this course, including water, exist as three-dimensional structures, it is useful to be able to draw them in a two-dimensional depiction; that is, to indicate their 3-D structure on a 2-D surface such as a piece of paper. This is often done with a wedge diagram. Wedge diagrams are simply conversions of Lewis structures that indicate which bonds are in the plane of the paper, which go "back" into it, and which come out of the page toward you. Straight lines are used for bonds in the same plane as the drawing. Dashed wedges (narrow triangles) are used to represent bonds going back into the page, and solid wedges are bonds coming out of the page toward you; the wider end of the wedge is the one nearer to you.

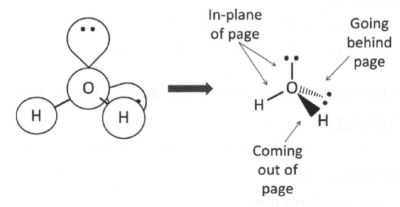

PROCEDURE CITATION

Begin your data and observations section for this experiment with a citation for the procedure you will follow.

PROCEDURE

You will work in pairs only for the purpose of sharing models; each person is to do their own work. Each pair will receive a model kit from the laboratory instructor. The model kit has enough parts to make all of the models without taking any apart. Leave all models built until you have finished the lab.

The model kits have specifically designed pieces to represent certain types of bonds and atoms. Use the following descriptions to help you accurately build your model.

Connectors

Short straight   2 electrons in single bonds or in a lone pair

Long flexible   2 electrons as part of a double bond

Atoms

The various model pieces used to represent atoms must be chosen to represent the correct type of electron pair geometry of the atom. Look at your Lewis structure. Count how many atoms and lone pairs of electrons there are around the atom. Then select the piece with the number of holes that corresponds to the number of groups around the central atom.

1-hole piece (white): Only used for hydrogen, linear

2-hole piece (red): Only used for oxygen, does not show lone pairs but accounts for lone pairs by the correct bond angle

4-hole piece: Tetrahedral electron pair geometry (black, blue, yellow, purple). Traditionally, black is used for carbon and blue for nitrogen

5-hole piece (brown): Trigonal bipyramidal (using all 5 holes) trigonal planar electron pair geometry (using 3 equatorial holes)

6-hole piece (gray): Octahedral electron pair geometry

For Each Model:

    a. Draw the Lewis structure

    b. Give the AX_mE_n type.

    c. Construct the model. Then make a wedge drawing of the model.

    d. Give the electron pair geometry.

    e. Give the molecular geometry of the molecule or ion.

    f. If the molecule or ion is polar, indicate the direction of the polarity on your wedge drawing, or state that it is non-polar.

    g. Answer any additional questions listed in complete sentences. Do not simply write the answer.

Model No. 1: H_2O (water)

g. What effect do the two unshared pairs of electrons have on the properties of water? Explain.

Model No. 2: NH_3 (ammonia)

Model No. 3: NH_4^+ (ammonium ion)

g. Does this ion have a dipole in addition to the overall positive charge? Explain.

Model No. 4: CH_4 (methane)

g. Apart from the identity of the central atom, what is the major difference between NH_4^+ and CH_4? How does this difference affect the relative solubility of the compounds in water? Explain.

Model No. 5: CO_2 (carbon dioxide)

Use tetrahedral atoms for both C and O. (black is usually used for C and red for O). Take four of the flexible connectors and attached them to the four holes on C. Attach the other end of two of these connectors to holes on one O and attach the remaining two connectors to holes on the other O.

Model No. 6: C_2H_6 (ethane)

Construct the model using the same methods used on the first 4 models. Answer a-e, treating each carbon atom in the molecule as a separate central atom.

g. Is the molecule planar? (flat) Explain.

Model No. 7: C_2H_4 (ethene)

Construct the model with a C=C double bond. Use 2 flexible connectors for the double bond as you did in model No. 5. Answer a-e, treating each carbon atom in the molecule as a separate central atom.

g. Is the molecule planar? Comment on the position of the hydrogens on one carbon compared to hydrogens on the other carbon.

Models No. 8 cis and 8 trans: $C_2H_2Cl_2$ (1,2 dichloroethene)

cis isomer: trans isomer:

Construct the model with a C=C double bond. Use 2 flexible connectors for the double bond as you did in model No. 5. Notice the position of the hydrogen and chlorine on one carbon compared to hydrogen and chlorine on the other carbon in each isomer. Answer a-e for both the cis and trans molecule. Treat each carbon as an independent central atom.

g. Based on your models, does it appear that rotation about the C=C bond requires little energy or a great deal of energy compared to rotation about the C-C bond in ethane, model No. 6?

Model No 9: PCl_5 (phosphorus pentachloride)

g. What are the bond angles? Are all of the chlorine atoms in the same environment or are their different environments? If the environments are different describe the environments and give the number of atoms in each environment. For the purpose of this question, "environment" can be described by the number of chlorine atoms that are nearest neighbors and the ClPCl angle to them from each Cl being considered.

Model No. 10: SO_4^{2-} (sulfate)

Write a Lewis structure of the sulfate ion with all single bonds and construct the model, then answer a-e.

Write the Lewis structure for sulfate ion with one double bond and three single bonds. Do not construct the model.

Write the Lewis structure for sulfate ion with two double bonds and two single bonds. Do not construct the model.

g. Explain whether or not the double bonds affect the electron pair geometry and molecular geometry.

Model No. 11: CO_3^{2-} **(carbonate)**

Model No. 12:   **PCl₃ (phosphorus trichloride)**

Model No. 13:   **SF₆ (sulfur hexafluoride)**

Clean-up

Put all pieces back into the box from which they came.

POST-LAB: RESULTS AND DISCUSSION

The requirements for your post-lab assignment will either be provided on-line or in a handout.

PREPARATION OF AN
IRON OXALATE COMPLEX

INTRODUCTION

One of the more interesting aspects of chemistry is the fact that two things can be mixed together to form a product that in no way resembles either of the reactants. This is similar to cooking; eggs, flour and sugar, for instance, do not individually look or taste like a cake. Also like cooking, the amounts of reagents and/or the conditions (e.g., temperature) used for the reaction can have a profound impact on the final result. Finally, both chefs and chemists try to predict the outcome of their cooking and experiments before they actually start to work on them.

The above analogies notwithstanding, chemistry experiments differ from cooking in a significant way: the conditions of a reaction are never deliberately manipulated to produce a specific result (note that we're discussing experiments here, not mass production of a chemical for sale). Whenever you cook something from a recipe, you most likely begin with an expectation of how the recipe is supposed to turn out. If the end result differs from this expectation, you could alter the amounts of ingredients used, or cook at a different temperature to make it turn out as it should. By contrast, science experiments begin with an idea, the hypothesis, for how something *may* occur and these ideas are followed by experiments to determine if the idea is correct. If you did an experiment and the results differed from what you expected, you would have to carefully analyze your data to figure out why. However, you would not try to force the results to agree with your prediction; after all, your hypothesis may or may not have been correct.

In order to determine why your predicted and experimental (observed) results were different, it is necessary to have detailed explanations of what was done and observed during each step of the experiment. Often minor or seemingly trivial variations in the procedure are the cause. Furthermore, since the results will not be known until after the experiment is complete, you do not know what might be important to make note of until after the fact, when it would be impossible to remember what exactly you did.

Each student who performs this experiment will follow nearly the same set of directions to prepare iron(III) oxalate crystals. However, one experimental parameter will be slightly different between students. This change will, potentially, alter the end result of your experiment. After you have prepared your solution, the following week you will compare your crystals with others. This will allow you to examine the effect this altered parameter has on crystal growth.

BACKGROUND

Many chemists devote much of their research to developing efficient syntheses for specific compounds. An efficient synthesis will take minimal time, produce the desired product with minimal contaminants, and yield the maximum amount of product for the amount of reagents used. Because they are so valuable, the processes used for the synthesis of many commercial compounds have been patented. In this experiment you will follow a synthesis protocol to produce an iron-containing compound. You will then isolate and purify your material by crystallization.

Crystallization

When a substance is crystallized, only a single compound will typically be present in the majority of the crystal. Thus, for substances that can be crystallized, it is an effective method of obtaining pure samples of them. Crystals form as the compound to be purified, the solute, slowly comes out of solution. As the molecules of it do so, they separate from the solvent molecules and congregate together in an orderly fashion. The rate at which the solute molecules come out of the solution often depends on their solubility in the solvent. If the compound is minimally soluble in the solvent, the molecules come out of solution quickly as a precipitate instead of a true crystal, along with a mixture of other substances present as contaminants. Conversely, slow crystallization leads to larger and purer crystals because the molecules have time to arrange themselves on the surface of the growing crystal, to the exclusion of contaminants.

Purity versus Yield

Although it may seem desirable for a product to be as pure as possible, there are situations where this is not the case. Whenever steps are taken to relieve a product of impurities, some of that product will tend to be lost as a result. For instance, consider a step in a synthesis procedure that calls for a precipitate to be washed. If the precipitate is washed several times, this may serve to rinse more impurities away, but there is a high likelihood that some of the desired compound will be washed away with them. Fewer washes will allow more product to be retained, but more of the impurities will be retained with it. The way that a product is made is therefore a compromise between purity and yield. In the experiment you are about to undertake, you will wash a precipitate you make with DI water to help remove some of the various impurities present in that precipitate.

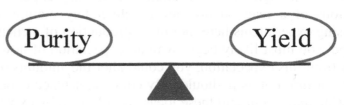

Figure 9.1. Synthesis reactions are, more often than not, a balance between purity and yield. In this balance, the one can only be increased at the expense of the other

In this experiment, the solubility of the product, $K_3Fe(C_2O_4)_3 \cdot 3H_2O$, can be altered by the addition of an alcohol to the aqueous reaction solution. You will use one of three different types of alcohol to do this: ethanol, 2-propanol (also known as rubbing alcohol), or 1-butanol. These three alcohols differ in the degree to which they are polar or non-polar, with ethanol being the most polar and 1-butanol the least:

Alcohol polarity: ethanol > 2-propanol > 1-butanol

Generally speaking, a certain amount of one of these alcohols should facilitate crystallization of the product, since $K_3Fe(C_2O_4)_3 \cdot 3H_2O$ is less soluble in an alcohol-water mixture. However, using a more-polar alcohol or a greater quantity of a less-polar one may also start the crystallization of oxalic acid, which is present as an excess reagent. If the oxalic acid crystallizes in this way, it will affect the purity of the $K_3Fe(C_2O_4)_3 \cdot 3H_2O$ crystals. This may be indicated by non-uniform crystal shapes and colors. You will discover the extent to which the alcohols affect the crystallization process for yourself when you analyze your results.

The chemistry of some of the procedural steps in the synthesis will be covered in your on-line pre-lab assignment.

Techniques

You will use a hot plate to heat solutions and separate precipitates from supernatants by decantation. Review how to properly use a hot plate and prevent your reaction mixture from "bumping", and how to properly decant in Appendix B.

PROCEDURE CITATION

Begin your data and observations section for this experiment with a citation for the procedure you will follow. See the section on citing sources in the "Laboratory Report Guidelines" chapter for information on how to properly cite a source.

PROCEDURE

As you perform this experiment, record the procedure exactly as you perform it and make complete observations. Although you must cite the lab manual in the usual way, you must also record the procedure as you do it. Each step of your procedure should have an accompanying observation that is as detailed as possible. Be sure to make a note of all the equipment and chemicals you use as well.

1. Acquire 3.5 g of iron(II) ammonium sulfate (ferrous ammonium sulfate). Do not weigh this. Instead, fill a test tube to the same level as the sample provided by your instructor.

2. Dissolve the solid in 25 mL of deionized (DI) water in a 250 mL beaker and stir well.

3. Add 25 mL of 1.0 M $H_2C_2O_4$ to the solution and heat to just below boiling (i.e., until you can just see steam coming off it) under your fume hood.

Continuously stir the mixture to prevent "bumping."

4. Cool the mixture and allow the precipitate to settle. Decant (see Appendix B) the liquid into a waste beaker.

5. Add about 20 mL of DI water to the precipitate. Briefly warm the mixture to aid washing and then allow the precipitate to settle again. Decant the wash liquid into the waste beaker and discard.

6. Add 7 mL of saturated $K_2C_2O_4$ (potassium oxalate) to the precipitate and warm the mixture to 40°C (use your thermometer to monitor the temperature). Remove your beaker from the hotplate when it reaches this temperature.

7. Acquire 16-17 mL of 3%-5% H_2O_2. Stir your solution, and *while you are stirring* add a few milliliters (the exact amount you add is unimportant, but try to add less than 3 mL) of the H_2O_2 solution and continue to stir. After about 15 seconds, add a few more milliliters and continue to stir. Keep doing this until you have added all of the H_2O_2 to the solution.

   - Be aware that this reaction is quite exothermic. Addition of even a few milliliters can cause the temperature to increase dramatically.

   - The H_2O_2 may be provided as a 3% solution, 5%, or anything in between. Note which you are given.

8. After all the H_2O_2 has been added, heat the mixture to just below a boil, then remove from heat.

9. Acquire 8 mL of 1.0 M $H_2C_2O_4$. Add about 1-2 mL of this to your solution and stir or swirl to mix for 15 seconds. Continue to add the $H_2C_2O_4$ in 1-2 mL increments and mix until the solution becomes clear and green; stop adding it when you get to this point.

   It is possible that the solution will either contain "leftover" residue from its reaction with the H_2O_2, or it will be mostly clear with a yellowish precipitate even if you add all 8 mL of the 1.0 M $H_2C_2O_4$. If either of these is the case, proceed as follows:

   - If the solution retains residue from its reaction with the H_2O_2, add another 2 mL of $H_2C_2O_4$ and mix.

   - If the solution is mostly green but has a yellowish, cloudy precipitate in it, add 1 mL of 3% H_2O_2. Continue adding H_2O_2 one mL at a time until it is clear, or until you have added a total of 5 mL.

10. Your TA will tell you to add a quantity of an alcohol mixture to aid the crystallization; different students will add different quantities of this mixture. Let your beaker cool until the outside of it is barely warm to the touch. Stir your solution, and while you are stirring add the alcohol to it.

- Use the dropper in the bottle to measure and dispense the alcohol; 1 dropper-full = 1 mL. Don't use a graduated cylinder.

11. Get a plastic cup and lid and write your name, section and the type and quantity of alcohol you added on the cup (do not write on the lid). Transfer your solution to this cup and store it in the designated area of the lab for your section.

12. Before your next lab period, complete the portions of the results and discussion section that are under the heading "complete the following . . . before you come to lab to observe your crystals." After you observe your crystals, you will be given 30 minutes to complete the remaining portions of the results and discussion. Be sure you leave sufficient room in your notebook to complete your crystal observations next lab period.

- Note: if you do not complete the required sections, you may not have time to finish your report next lab period. The standard late penalty will apply in this case.

Next Lab Period . . .

13. Describe your crystals. Make a sketch of one of your "good" crystals.

- If you don't have any crystals, look at someone else's. Note how much alcohol they added.

14. Compare the size and quantity of your crystals to several other students' crystals, noting the type and quantity of alcohol they each added and whose they are. Look for trends or patterns in the different crystal samples you observe (e.g., "samples treated with __mL of alcohol X tended to have lots of small crystals") and note them.

- You must observe at least one example of each of the different type and amounts alcohols that were added.

- If you want to keep your crystals, ask your TA for a sample vial.

Clean-up

15. Unplug your hot plate.

16. Clean all glassware with detergent, rinse well with cold water, and let dry on your towel.

17. Wipe-up any spills and dispose of garbage.

POST-LAB: RESULTS AND DISCUSSION

The requirements for your post-lab assignment will either be provided on-line or in a handout.

ANALYSIS OF BLEACH BY IODOMETRY

INTRODUCTION

Titrations can be used to determine the concentrations of a variety of different unknown solutions. Their versatility is partly due to the fact they can utilize different types of chemical reactions to fit the specific requirements of a given experiment. The "Molar Mass of a Known Acid" lab that was used to introduce the technique was an acid-base titration that involved a neutralization reaction of an acid with a base. This laboratory experiment utilizes an oxidation-reduction, or redox, titration in which a compound is reduced upon addition of the titrant. You will use this technique to determine the concentration of sodium hypochlorite in a solution. Hypochlorite is the reactive ingredient in commercial bleach.

BACKGROUND

Note: If you are unfamiliar with the fundamentals of titrations, see the background to the "Molar Mass of a Known Acid" lab. You are responsible for knowing this information even if you have not done this experiment.

The bleaching action of many household cleansers is due to the oxidizing strength of sodium hypochlorite ($NaClO$). This compound is commonly used to whiten laundry, as a microbial disinfectant, and also to treat water so that it is safe to drink. The use of hypochlorite as a sanitizing agent dates back to at least the mid-nineteenth century (albeit as its calcium salt rather than the sodium).

Your objective in this experiment is to determine the concentration of a sodium hypochlorite/bleach solution. This will actually require two separate reactions. First, an excess of iodide (I^-) will be added to the bleach. Hypochlorite will then oxidize the iodide to iodine:

$$ClO^-(aq) + 2\,H^+(aq) + 2\,I^-(aq) \rightarrow Cl^-(aq) + H_2O(l) + I_2(aq)$$

In the second step, "iodometry" is used to determine the concentration of the iodine produced in this reaction. Iodometry is the determination of the concentration of iodine by redox titration with the reducing agent thiosulfate.

$$2\,S_2O_3{}^{2-}(aq) + I_2(aq) \rightarrow S_4O_6{}^{2-}(aq) + 2\,I^-(aq)$$

Put together, this series of equations can be represented in the following diagram:

First
Excess iodide is used to "convert" all of the hypochlorite in solution to chloride and iodine.

$$ClO^- + 2\,H^+ + 2\,I^- \rightarrow Cl^- + H_2O + \boxed{I_2}$$

Then
The iodine produced in the first reaction is titrated with thiosulfate

$$2\,S_2O_3{}^{2-} + I_2 \rightarrow S_4O_6{}^{2-} + 2\,I^-$$

By knowing how much thiosulfate is required to reach the equivalence point of this titration, it is possible to calculate how much iodine was produced from the oxidation of iodide. By knowing how much iodine was so produced, it is possible to calculate how much sodium hypochlorite was present in the original bleach solution.

You will note that this titration determines the number of moles (or concentration) of iodine, not the analyte of interest, hypochlorite. Because iodide was added to the sample, not iodine, all of the iodine in the solution comes from the reaction between hypochlorite and iodide. Thus, the moles of iodine in the solution are equal to the moles of hypochlorite that reacted. Provided that an excess of iodide was added so that all the hypochlorite reacted, the number of moles of iodine found in the sample is equal to the number of moles of hypochlorite.

Aqueous iodine solutions are brown in color, so iodine can act as its own endpoint indicator. However, the endpoint can be made easier to detect by adding starch to the solution because it forms an intense blue-purple complex with iodine.

Technically, what is actually in a solution of bleach is *sodium* hypochlorite, not simply hypochlorite. In our discussion of the chemistry used in this lab, we referred to this compound as "hypochlorite" to better emphasize the changes this compound, as well as bromate and thiosulfate, undergo during the titration. However, since all anions need to be balanced by a cation, the hypochlorite used here actually exists as its sodium salt.

Iodometry Titration Primary Standard

Thiosulfate is available commercially as sodium thiosulfate pentahydrate, but since crystals of it contain varying amounts of water, it is not a good primary standard. Furthermore, solutions of thiosulfate are not stable for long periods of time because they are decomposed by acids and bacteria. Therefore, these solutions must be prepared and standardized just prior to use.

The thiosulfate used in this experiment can be standardized by a two-step reaction series that is somewhat similar to the two reactions described above. In the first of these, a standard solution of bromate—one that has been carefully made to a known concentration—will be oxidized by excess iodide to bromide and iodine. Note the similarities between this reaction and the oxidation of iodide by hypochlorite above.

$$BrO_3^-(aq) + 6 H^+(aq) + 6 I^-(aq) \rightarrow Br^-(aq) + 3 H_2O(l) + 3 I_2(aq)$$

In the second reaction, the iodine produced in this reaction is reduced by thiosulfate back to iodide; this is identical to the second reaction above. Because 1 mole of bromate produces 3 moles of iodine and each mole of iodine reacts with 2 moles of thiosulfate, 1 mole of bromate is equivalent to 6 moles of thiosulfate. Put together, the net reaction is:

$$BrO_3^-(aq) + 6 H^+(aq) + 6 S_2O_3^{2-}(aq) \rightarrow Br^-(aq) + 3S_4O_6^{2-}(aq) + 3 H_2O(l)$$

In summary, your approach to this experiment will be to first standardize a solution of sodium thiosulfate with a known, standard solution of potassium bromate. This thiosulfate solution will then be used to determine the concentration of two sodium hypochlorite solutions: a known and an unknown. In neither case will the thiosulfate be used to directly titrate the bromate or hypochlorite.

Calculations

Similar to many of the calculations you have performed in this course, there is more than one way to take the data you will acquire in this experiment and arrive at the concentration of sodium hypochlorite in your bleach solution. The following example represents just one way of doing this.

The various calculations you will need to perform to determine the concentration of your bleach solution can be divided into two groups. The first group consists of those calculations performed to determine the concentration of the thiosulfate solution. These calculations will make use of the titration data acquired during the standardization of the sodium thiosulfate solution. The second group of calculations will make use of the titration data acquired to determine the concentration of the bleach solution itself.

Standardization of Thiosulfate Solution

For this first example, let's say 17.34 mL of a thiosulfate solution are required to titrate the iodine produced from the reaction of excess iodide and 15.00 mL of a 0.1713 M $KBrO_3$ solution.

The first step in determining the concentration of the thiosulfate solution is to determine how many moles of $KBrO_3$ were present in the 15.00 mL of it used. If you do this calculation for yourself, you should arrive at 2.570×10^{-3} moles of $KBrO_3$. This information, and the reaction stoichiometry between this compound and iodine, can be used to determine how many moles of iodine were produced from the reaction of potassium bromate and excess I^-:

$$2.570 \times 10^{-3} \text{ mol } \cancel{KBrO_3} \times \frac{3 \text{ } I_2}{1 \text{ } \cancel{KBrO_3}} = 0.007710 \text{ moles } I_2$$

The reaction stoichiometry between iodine and thiosulfate can then be used to determine how many moles of thiosulfate reacted with these moles of iodine:

$$0.007710 \text{ moles } \cancel{I_2} \times \frac{2 \text{ } S_2O_3^{2-}}{1 \text{ } \cancel{I_2}} = 0.01420 \text{ moles } S_2O_3^{2-}$$

Since 0.01420 moles of thiosulfate were present in the 17.34 mL of it used in the titration, the concentration of the thiosulfate solution must be 0.8189 M.

Molarity of Sodium Hypochlorite

The calculations performed to determine the concentration of a sodium hypochlorite solution are similar to those involved in the standardization of the thiosulfate solution, but are performed in the reverse order. Let's say that 13.48 mL of the thiosulfate solution we determined the concentration of are required to titrate the iodine produced from the reaction of excess iodine and the sodium hypochlorite in 15.00 mL of unknown sodium hypochlorite solution.

The first step in determining the concentration of the NaClO solution is to determine how many moles of $S_2O_3^{2-}$ were present in the 13.48 mL of it used in the titration. If you do this calculation for yourself, you should arrive at 0.01104 moles of $S_2O_3^{2-}$.

Once the moles of thiosulfate used in the titration is known, the reaction stoichiometry between this compound and I_2 can be used to calculate how many moles of I_2 were present for it to react with. This will also tell us what quantity of I_2 was produced from the reaction of NaClO and excess I^-.

$$0.01104 \text{ moles } \cancel{S_2O_3^{2-}} \times \frac{1 \text{ } I_2}{2 \text{ } \cancel{S_2O_3^{2-}}} = 0.005520 \text{ moles } I_2$$

The reaction stoichiometry between NaClO and I_2 is 1:1, so 0.005520 moles of NaClO must have reacted to produce these 0.005520 moles of I_2 :

$$0.005520 \text{ moles } \cancel{I_2} \times \frac{1 \text{ } NaClO}{1 \text{ } \cancel{I_2}} = 0.005520 \text{ moles } NaClO$$

Finally, the concentration of the NaClO solution can be calculated. We know that 0.00520 moles of it are present in 15.00 mL, so its molarity is 0.3467 M (.00520 mol / .01500 L).

Mass Percent of Sodium Hypochlorite

Although solution concentrations are commonly reported in molarity in laboratory settings, the concentration of bleach solutions sold in stores are typically given as a mass percent figure. The mass percent of a solution is the percentage of its total mass that is solute. They can be calculated by dividing the mass of solute known to be in a given mass of solution and multiplying by 100%. If you do this for a solution that contains 2 grams of solute for every 100 grams of solution, you will find its mass percent to be 2%.

A concentration in molarity can be converted to a mass percent provided the molar mass of the solute and the density of the solution are both known. The molar mass of the solute in our bleach solution, NaClO, is 74.44 grams per mole. For the purposes of this experiment, we can assume this solution has the same density as water.

We can begin our calculation of the solution's mass percent sodium hypochlorite by first determining how many moles of sodium hypochlorite are present per liter of solution. Since we have a 0.3467 M solution, this will be 0.3467 moles. This number of moles can then be converted into a mass of NaClO:

$$0.3467 \ \cancel{mol} \ x \ \frac{74.44 \text{ g}}{1 \ \cancel{mol}} = 25.81 \text{ grams NaClO}$$

Now that we know how many grams of NaClO are present in each liter of solution, we need to know how many total grams of solution are present. Since the solution has a density of 1.00 g/mL, one liter (1000 mL) of solution has a mass of 1000 grams:

$$1000 \ \cancel{mL} \ x \ \frac{1.00 \text{ g}}{1 \ \cancel{mL}} = 1000 \text{ g}$$

Finally, the mass percent of our solution can be calculated:

$$\frac{25.81 \text{ g}}{1000 \text{ g}} \ x \ 100\% = 2.581\%$$

PROCEDURE CITATION

Begin your data and observations section for this experiment with a citation for the procedure you will follow.

PROCEDURE

Most of the data you record in this lab will consist of numerical measurements, though you will also make some qualitative observations as well. You will do a minimum of three titrations of the potassium bromate solution, and three of bleach.

As you perform this experiment, make a note of all the equipment and chemicals you use. Be sure to include the size of all volumetric glassware and give a description of all the reagents you use.

Part A: Set Up

1. Fill your weighing bottle about 80% full of sodium thiosulfate pentahydrate, $Na_2S_2O_3 \cdot 5H_2O$. Add this to a beaker and dissolve in about 250 mL of deionized water. Mix the solution thoroughly until all of the solid dissolves.

2. Rinse (Appendix B) and fill a burette with the thiosulfate solution. Clamp the burette in a burette clamp and place a waste beaker below it.

3. Fill the burette with the thiosulfate solution. Follow the remaining guidelines as provided in Appendix B to prepare it for dispensing this solution.

    •   Note that a portion of the credit you receive for your burette data will depend on reading it correctly and making appropriate initial and final readings.

Part B: Standardization of Sodium Thiosulfate Solution

4. Put about 50 mL of the potassium bromate solution in a small clean dry beaker.

5. Put a scoopula, about 2 cm full, of solid KI into 4 clean, dry 250 mL Erlenmeyer flask. Add approximately 50 mL of deionized water. Stir until the KI dissolves.

6. Add 2 dropper-fulls of 3 M H_2SO_4 to each of the 4 Erlenmeyer flasks.

7. Rinse (Appendix B) a 10.00 mL volumetric pipette with the potassium bromate solution twice.

8. Use the pipette to transfer an aliquot of the potassium bromate solution into ONE of the 250 mL Erlenmeyer flasks. The solution should turn brown. Proceed to the titration immediately; oxygen from the air will compromise your results if your solution is allowed to sit too long.

9. Titrate this first sample quickly, swirling the Erlenmeyer flask as you add the thiosulfate solution from the burette. Stop adding thiosulfate when the solution has cleared a little, but is still somewhat dark in color.

10. Add two drops of starch solution. The solution should become darker upon addition of the starch.

11. Add thiosulfate solution drop-wise, swirling the flask in between each addition. Use your deionized water bottle to rinse any drops hanging from the tip of the burette into the Erlenmeyer flask. When the solution remains colorless after swirling the flask, you have reached the endpoint.

    • This rough titration is done quickly to get an approximation of the endpoint.

12. Refill the burette and again prepare it for dispensing.

13. Pipette an aliquot of the potassium bromate solution into a second Erlenmeyer flask with KI and H_2SO_4 in it.

14. When you titrate this second flask, add all but approximately 2 mL the volume of thiosulfate that was needed to titrate the first sample.

15. Add two drops of starch solution and continue the titration until the solution just barely remains colorless after swirling the flask. Place a piece of white paper under the flask to make the color change more visible.

16. Prepare and titrate your third and forth flasks.

17. Open the Excel file named "Titration" in the 105 folder on your computer's desktop. Enter your burette data into this and note the average and standard deviation it provides you.

18. Pour the contents of your four reaction flasks (the Erlenmeyer flasks) into the waste container in the fume hood. Rinse these flasks thoroughly. *Do not discard the sodium thiosulfate solution.* You will need it to complete parts C and D.

Part C: Determination of Known Bleach

19. Clean and prepare your 4 Erlenmeyer flasks as you did in part A, with a scoop of KI, approximately 50 mL of deionized water, and two droppers of 3 M H_2SO_4.

20. Obtain about 100 mL of known bleach solution.

21. Clean your volumetric pipette and rinse it with the bleach solution.

22. Use the pipette to transfer an aliquot of the bleach solution into an Erlenmeyer flask with the KI and H_2SO_4. Titrate immediately as you did in part A. Be sure to add starch as you did for the standardization of thiosulfate part. This first titration in part C is a rough titration.

23. Repeat the previous two steps on the three remaining flask to obtain three sets of "careful" titration data.

24. Enter your burette data into the Excel spreadsheet and note the average and standard deviation it provides you.

Part D: Determination of Unknown Bleach

25. Your TA will assign you one of the unknown bleach solutions to titrate. Follow the procedure in the previous part to do this.

Part E: Clean-up

26. Dispose of all remaining solutions in the waste container in the fume hood.

27. Wash all glassware with detergent, rinse thoroughly with water, and place on your towel to dry.

28. Clean-up all spills and throw all garbage in the garbage cans.

POST-LAB: CALCULATIONS

Part B

1. Use your data from part B to calculate the concentration of the sodium thiosulfate solution you made in moles/L. You will perform this calculation three times, once for each trial.

2. Average the thiosulfate concentrations you just calculated.

3. Use the equation for the standard deviation provided in the experiment "Laboratory Techniques" to calculate the standard deviation of your thiosulfate concentrations.

4. Calculate the range your standard deviation falls around your average thiosulfate concentration by adding one standard deviation to this average and subtracting one from it.

Parts C and D

NOTE: you will perform all of the following calculations twice, once for the known bleach solution and once for the unknown.

1. Calculate the molarity of sodium hypochlorite in the two bleach solutions (the known and the unknown), three times for each. Use the average thiosulfate concentration you calculated previously to do this.

2. Convert the concentrations of the two bleach solutions from molarity to mass percentages. Assume the solutions have the same density as water.

3. Average the three percentages from the known solution and the three for the unknown.

4. Calculate the standard deviation of the mass percentages for the known and again for the unknown.

5. Calculate the ranges your standard deviations fall around their associated averages by adding one standard deviation to the average and subtracting one from it.

POST-LAB: RESULTS AND DISCUSSION

The remaining requirements for your post-lab assignment will either be provided on-line or in a handout.

LIMITING REACTANT

INTRODUCTION

The Food and Drug Administration (FDA) puts regulations on how much iron can be added to fortified cereal, the maximum amount of aspirin that each pill can contain, and requires labels on milk cartons to indicate how much of the daily recommended calcium there is in a glass of the milk. However, since the farmer that milks the cow does not know exactly how much calcium there is in each gallon of milk the cow produces, how does the dairy know what calcium-content value to print on the carton? The milk must be analyzed to determine its calcium content.

One method for determining how much of a specific element or compound is in a mixture is gravimetric analysis. In this type of analysis, the component of interest is first separated from the remaining constituents of the mixture by precipitation. For example, all the calcium in a sample glass of milk can be removed from the milk by adding a reagent that is known to form a known solid compound with calcium but not the other ingredients of milk. This precipitate can then be filtered out of the mixture and its mass determined. As long as the molar mass of it is known, the number of moles of it, and more importantly the compound of interest, can be calculated.

BACKGROUND

In this experiment you will be given a solid sample that is a mixture of two water-soluble solid salts: Na_2CO_3 and $CaCl_2 \cdot 2H_2O$. When this mixture is dissolved in water, both salts will dissociate into their respective ions. Once in solution, the ions are free to move about and may associate with other ions in solution to again form salts. However, any soluble salts will immediately dissociate again and remain as ions in solution. On the other hand, the insoluble salt $CaCO_3$ precipitates out of solution when calcium and carbonate ions encounter each other.

Hydrated Salts (Hydrates)

When ionic compounds crystallize from aqueous solution, it is common for them to trap water molecules in the crystal lattice. Because these water molecules contribute to the mass of the compound when it is measured, they must be included in the formula (and the molar mass) of the compound. The ratio of water to the ions is fixed for each compound. The extra water molecules are indicated in the formula by putting a dot ($\cdot$) after the formula followed by the number of water molecules associated with each formula unit of the compound.

Stoichiometry

The insoluble salt that will be precipitated in this lab is $CaCO_3$. The overall balanced equation is:

$$Na_2CO_3 \text{ (aq)} + CaCl_2 \cdot 2\,H_2O \text{ (aq)} \rightarrow CaCO_3 \text{ (s)} + 2\,NaCl \text{ (aq)} + 2\,H_2O \text{ (l)}$$

Since the only reagent containing calcium is $CaCl_2 \cdot 2H_2O$, all of the calcium in the $CaCO_3$ precipitate must come from this compound. Also notice that the only source of carbonate is from Na_2CO_3. Thus, the coefficients in the balanced chemical equation can be used to calculate the amount of product that can be made from a certain amount of reactants. It takes one mole of Na_2CO_3, and one of $CaCl_2 \cdot 2H_2O$, to make one mole of $CaCO_3$ product. Working from the other direction, in order to make one mole of $CaCO_3$, you would one mole of Na_2CO_3 and one mole of $CaCl_2 \cdot 2H_2O$:

$$1 \text{ mol CaCO}_3 \text{ x } \frac{1 \text{ mol Na}_2\text{CO}_3}{1 \text{ mol CaCO}_3} = 1 \text{ mol Na}_2\text{CO}_3$$

$$1 \text{ mol CaCO}_3 \text{ x } \frac{1 \text{ mol CaCl}_2 \cdot 2\text{H}_2\text{O}}{1 \text{ mol CaCO}_3} = 1 \text{ mol CaCl}_2 \cdot 2\text{H}_2\text{O}$$

The concept of using a balanced equation to figure out how many moles of product can be made from a certain number of moles of reactants is called stoichiometry. Mole-to-mole ratios are used to "convert" moles of one reactant or product into another reactant or product.

Limiting Reactant

Stoichiometry can be used to demonstrate that it takes one mole of $CaCl_2 \cdot 2H_2O$ to produce one mole of $CaCO_3$:

$$1 \text{ mol CaCl}_2 \cdot 2\text{H}_2\text{O} \text{ x } \frac{1 \text{ mol CaCO}_3}{1 \text{ mol CaCl}_2 \cdot 2\text{H}_2\text{O}} = 1 \text{ mol CaCO}_3$$

This same technique can also be used to show it takes one mole of Na_2CO_3 to do the same:

$$1 \text{ mol Na}_2\text{CO}_3 \text{ x } \frac{1 \text{ mol CaCO}_3}{1 \text{ mol Na}_2\text{CO}_3} = 1 \text{ mol CaCO}_3$$

Put another way, the synthesis of one mole of $CaCO_3$ requires one mole of $CaCl_2 \cdot 2H_2O$ and one mole of Na_2CO_3.

Now consider what would happen if 1.0 mol of Na_2CO_3 is mixed with 2.0 mol of $CaCl_2 \cdot 2H_2O$. Since it takes 1 mol of Na_2CO_3 to make 1 of $CaCO_3$, and 1 mol of Na_2CO_3 has been provided, a maximum of 1.0 mol of $CaCO_3$ can be synthesized. Meanwhile, because the synthesis of 1 mol of $CaCO_3$ only requires 1 mol of $CaCl_2 \cdot 2H_2O$, but 2.0 mol of this has been provided, the reaction will finish with 1.0 mol of $CaCl_2 \cdot 2H_2O$ left-over. In chemical reactions, reagents that were present in excess before the reaction started, and so are left-over when it finishes, are called excess reagents. Conversely, the reagent that is totally consumed, and so limits the amount of product that can be made, is called the limiting reagent.

If the quantities of both reagents that take part in a reaction can be measured, it is readily possible to calculate which is the excess reagent and which is the limiting. However, there are times when such measurements are difficult or impossible. In this case, this determination can be made by analyzing the products of the reaction after it is completed. Naturally, the excess reagent will be present amongst the products but the limiting reagent will not.

In this experiment, you will be able to analyze the products of your reaction, and therefore determine which reagent is in excess, by taking advantage of their precipitation chemistry. If you are provided with a mixture that contains $CaCl_2 \cdot 2H_2O$ in excess, then after the reaction is completed, additional $CaCO_3$ precipitate will form if more Na_2CO_3 is added to the solution the reaction took place in. However, no such precipitate would form if extra $CaCl_2 \cdot 2H_2O$ were added instead. Conversely, if Na_2CO_3 is in excess, then more precipitate would form if extra $CaCl_2 \cdot 2H_2O$ were added but not if extra Na_2CO_3 were added.

Moles versus Grams

Moles are not a practical measurement in the laboratory because we cannot see individual molecules, making them difficult to count out. Besides, trying to count out 6.022×10^{23} (molecules per mole) would take too long. Assuming you counted at a rate of 1 molecule per second, it would require more than 19 quadrillion—or more than 19,000 trillion—years! However, mass is a quantity that can easily be determined in the lab. Moles are converted into grams using molar masses:

$$1 \text{ mol } CaCl_2 \cdot 2H_2O \times \frac{147.00 \text{ g } CaCl_2 \cdot 2H_2O}{1 \text{ mol } CaCl_2 \cdot 2H_2O} = 147.0 \text{ g } CaCl_2 \cdot 2H_2O$$

Balanced reactions only tell the mole-to-mole ratio between reactants and products, not the gram-to-gram ratio, so you must compare moles, not grams, when determining the limiting reactant.

For example, if you had 200.0 grams of each $CaCl_2 \cdot 2H_2O$ and Na_2CO_3, which of the reactants is the limiting reactant? First convert both masses to moles (1.360 mol $CaCl_2 \cdot 2H_2O$ and 1.887 mol Na_2CO_3) and then use the mole-to-mole ratios to calculate the amount of product that can be made. $CaCl_2 \cdot 2H_2O$ is the limiting reactant because 200.0 g of $CaCl_2 \cdot 2H_2O$ produces only 1.360 mol of $CaCO_3$, while 200.0 g Na_2CO_3, could produce 1.887 mol $CaCO_3$. Try this calculation on your own and make sure you get the same numbers.

You will be doing similar calculations using balanced chemical reactions throughout your chemistry career and in all cases you must convert to moles before using a mole-to-mole ratio, the fundamental application of stoichiometry.

In this experiment you are to determine how much of each of the two reacting salts was in your unknown salt mixture based on the mass of the $CaCO_3$ precipitate you make. This is a stoichiometry problem in which you calculate the amount of reactant originally present (eggs used) from product made (dozens of cookies). This is the reverse of the calculation shown above where product made was calculated from reactant available. However, the principle is the same: use mole-to-mole ratios. The sequence of calculations is given to you in the calculations section. However, you must be able to explain the concept and solve similar problems throughout your chemistry education.

Percentages

Percentages are ratios multiplied by 100. Thus, the units of the two numbers in the ratio must cancel. The result is a percentage in terms of the unit used. If the unit is grams, the result is a percentage by mass. For example, the calcium chloride is provided as a hydrated salt, meaning it has water molecules associated with it. These water molecules contribute to the mass of the salt when you weigh it. What percentage of the mass of a sample of $CaCl_2 \cdot 2H_2O$ is due to the water molecules present? We can start out with the mole-to-mole ratio of 2 moles of H_2O per 1 mole of $CaCl_2 \cdot 2H_2O$, but because we want to know what the percent mass is, the units that must cancel need to be for mass. First convert moles to grams. You should be able to calculate the mass of 2 moles of water and the mass of 1 mole of $CaCl_2 \cdot 2H_2O$ was calculated above for you, 147.0 g/mol. Now, the ratio of the mass of water to $CaCl_2 \cdot 2H_2O$ is used to calculate percent mass of water in 1 mole of the $CaCl_2 \cdot 2H_2O$ salt:

$$\frac{2 \text{ mol } H_2O}{1 \text{ mol } CaCl_2 \cdot 2H_2O} = \frac{36.03 \text{ g } H_2O}{147.00 \text{ g } CaCl_2 \cdot 2H_2O} \times 100 = \begin{array}{l} 24.51\% \text{ } H_2O \text{ in } CaCl_2 \cdot 2H_2O \\ \text{by mass, or } 24.51 \text{ g } H_2O \text{ per} \\ 100 \text{ g } CaCl_2 \cdot 2H_2O \end{array}$$

Any percentage can be calculated in the same way so long as the units in the ratio (grams in this example) are the same.

Techniques

You will be using a hot plate to heat your solutions, weighing by difference, and decanting. A description of how to properly do these techniques is in Appendix B. You will be introduced to the technique of filtering in this lab.

PROCEDURE CITATION

Begin your data and observations section for this experiment with a citation for the procedure you will follow. See the section on citing sources in the "Laboratory Report Guidelines" chapter for information on how to properly cite a source.

PROCEDURE

Most of the data you record in this lab will consist of numerical measurements, though you will also make some qualitative observations as well. All your data must be clearly labeled so the reader can follow the numbers without referring to the procedures in the laboratory manual (see the Laboratory Report Guidelines for instructions and an example of how all data should be recorded). In this experiment you will do two trials at the same time. Make sure you clearly indicate which data goes with which trial.

Part A: Precipitation of $CaCO_3$

1. Label two clean 150 mL beakers "Trial 1" and "Trial 2".

2. Your TA will give you a plastic bottle that contains either an unknown mixture of $CaCl_2 \cdot 2H_2O/Na_2CO_3$, or a known mixture of known composition. Record which you are given.

3. Use the method of weighing by difference (Appendix B) to transfer about half of your salt mixture into each of your two beakers. It is not important that the two masses are the same, as long as you know which was dispensed in which beaker.

4. Add approximately 50 mL of deionized water to each beaker. Stir the mixtures with separate stirring rods for about 1 minute. Keep the stirring rods in the beakers at all times.

5. Clean and label two watch glasses with "Trial 1" and "Trial 2," using labeling tape. Cover each beaker with the appropriate watch glass without removing your stir rods.

6. Place one beaker on your hot plate under your bench top fume hood and heat the solution to 90°C, continuously stirring as it warms. Keep it at this temperature and continue to stir for 3 minutes.

7. Remove the beaker from the heat and let it stand at room temperature for 5 minutes. Use a stream of water from a wash bottle to rinse the thermometer directing the rinse into the beaker. Set the thermometer on a towel.

8. Place the beaker in an ice bath to expedite the cooling. Be careful not to let it tip over or get water from the ice bath in it. Let it sit in the ice bath for about 10 minutes

9. Repeat the previous three steps (the heating, stirring, and cooling) with your other beaker.

10. While your beakers are cooling, you may start to set up your filtering apparatus as directed in part B. Once your beakers are cool, allow the precipitate to settle and do not disturb it.

Part B: Filtering

11. Label one piece of filter paper with "Trial 1" and the other "Trial 2" using pencil. Label both with your name.

12. Fold the filter papers in half so that the name is on the inside. Tear off one small corner of both folded papers. Fold the papers again to form a quarter-circle.

13. Place the filter paper labeled trial 1 on the dry watch glass for trial 1 and weigh the two together. Repeat for trial 2.

   • Keep track of which watch glass was used for which trial. This will be important later.

14. Open the papers to form a cone that excludes the torn corner (see figure, the torn corner should be on the outside of the cone). Place each filter paper cup into a funnel and seal them to the sides of the funnels with a small amount of deionized water. Place each funnel over an Erlenmeyer flask. Put a piece of labeling tape on the Erlenmeyer flasks and label with the same trial number as the filter paper they hold. Have your TA check your filtering set-up.

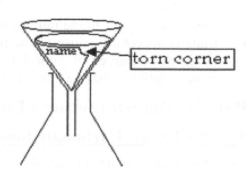

15. If your solutions from part A are clear, decant (see Appendix B) the solution from each trial into the appropriate labeled flask. Do not overflow the filter paper cup or solution will pass between the filter paper and sides of the funnel.

   • Take a moment to check that you are pouring the correct trial precipitate into the correct funnel.

16. Let most of the solution drain through before adding more sample to the filter paper. As the solutions drain and room becomes available, continue to pour until all the solution has been filtered.

17. Rinse any precipitate from the beaker's walls with a stream of water from a wash bottle while holding the beaker tipped over the filter. Do not forget to wash off any stirring rods used.

18. Rinse the precipitates by adding deionized water to the filter and letting it drain. Spraying it for about 5 seconds with your wash bottle should be sufficient. This helps to remove any impurities that may remain "stuck" to the precipitate or filter paper.

For all subsequent steps, be very careful that you do not lose any precipitate.

19. Carefully remove the filter papers and precipitates from the funnel. Fold each paper in half and place them on a paper towel to absorb some of the remaining water.

20. Add one dropper-full of 1.0 M HCl to both beakers you used for this part, then fill them about 20% full with DI water. Stir the beakers' contents to mix, then put them aside.

Part C: Drying the Precipitate

21. Gently pat dry your filter paper and precipitate. The more excess water you are able to remove with the paper towels, the faster the drying process will go.

22. Carefully transfer each of your filter papers to the same watch glass they were weighed on at the beginning of part B. Gently open the papers so that the precipitate is facing up.

23. Place the watch glasses with the filter papers and precipitates in the microwave for 5-10 seconds to aid drying. Your TA will monitor this process.

> **When microwaving, do not let your precipitate, or anyone else's, get too hot.**
>
> **They can "pop" or catch fire.**

24. Using a paper towel, carefully remove the hot watch glasses from the microwave and let the papers cool to room temperature. Dry off any moisture that may have condensed on the watch glass.

25. If the samples are not dry, microwave for another 10 seconds. You can continue to do 10-second intervals in the microwave, but be sure the papers cool to room temperature between each time and that you place them in the microwave with others' that are at approximately the same dryness.

26. Once you believe your precipitate is dry, let it cool to room temperature, wipe any moisture from the watch glass, and weigh both the paper and watch glass.

Do not weigh samples while they are hot.

27. Dry your samples in the microwave for another 10 seconds, and reweigh them. If the mass for one of your trials is acceptably close to the previous mass for that trial, you are done with that trial. The acceptable range will be given by your TA. If the mass is not close enough to your last mass, continue drying each sample until you have a consistent mass for that trial.

Part D: Determination of the Limiting Reactant

Test for Excess Carbonate Ions

28. Observe the solution from filtering trial 1 and note the degree of cloudiness.

29. Add one full dropper of 0.5 M Ca^{2+} (0.5 M $CaCl_2$ solution) to the solution from filtering trial 1 and wait 2 minutes. Note what happens to the contents of the flask.

Test for Excess Calcium Ions

30. Observe the solution from filtering trial 2. Carefully note the degree of cloudiness.

31. Add one full dropper of 0.5 M CO_3^{2-} (0.5 M Na_2CO_3 solution) to the solution from filtering trial 2 and wait 2 minutes. As for the trial 1 flask, note what happens to the contents of the trial 2 flask.

32. If no precipitate forms in either flask after 5 minutes, add another full dropper of the appropriate solution to each flask.

33. After you have established the presence of a precipitate in one of the flasks, rinse them both out. Add one dropper-full of 1.0 M HCl to both of them, then fill them about 20% full with DI water. Swirl to mix and set the flasks aside.

Part E: Clean-up

34. Place the dried precipitate/filter paper and any excess mixture in the provided bag in the fume hood.

35. Rinse-out the beakers and flasks you added the HCl and water to. Pour all other solutions down the drain and flush with plenty of cold water.

36. Turn off and unplug your hotplate.

37. Clean all glassware with the provided detergent, rinse with plenty of cold water, and place it on your towel to dry.

38. Clean-up all spills and dispose of garbage.

Wash your hands thoroughly before eating or drinking anything or touching your face.

Part F: Collaborator Data

If you were given a known, collect the following data from someone else who was given an unknown. If you were given an unknown, collect the same from someone who was given a known:

- The unknown number (if applicable)

- Mass data from when the mixture was transferred into the beakers in part A

- Initial filter paper masses from part B

- Final filter paper + precipitate masses from part C

- Excess ion observations from part D

POST-LAB: CALCULATIONS

For each trial, including the two you performed and the two your collaborator performed, calculate each of the items listed below. For all calculations that are repeated for separate trials, you must show a complete calculation at least once in your notebook. See the Laboratory Report Guidelines, "Calculations" for how to properly set up this section of your lab report. Make sure all numbers are labeled and have units.

1. Mass of the solid mixture used.

2. Mass of $CaCO_3$ precipitate.

3. Use your results from part D to determine which reactant was limiting in the mixture. Based on this, calculate the mass of the limiting reactant present in the original mixture.

4. Mass of the non-limiting reactant present in the mixture.

5. Percent mass of each reactant in the solid mixture.

6. For the unknown salt mixture, average the percent masses from your two trials. Do the same for the known salt mixture.

7. Use the standard deviation provided in the background to the experiment "Laboratory Techniques" to calculate the standard deviation of your percent masses for your unknown salt. Do the same for the known salt.

POST-LAB: RESULTS AND DISCUSSION

The remaining requirements for your post-lab assignment will either be provided on-line or in a handout.

ANALYSIS OF IRON BY OXIDATION-REDUCTION TITRATION

INTRODUCTION

Many transition metal cations can have more than one possible charge (Worksheet 1). Differently charged species of the same element can have different chemical and physical properties. Knowing the charge can allow separation of the different ions based on their properties. For example, Cu^{2+} is blue and stable in solution, while Cu^+ is colorless and reacts with oxygen. Hemoglobin contains iron as Fe^{2+}, but it is inactive at binding oxygen when the iron gets oxidized to Fe^{3+}. There are many similar situations in which it is important to always properly indicate charges of ions.

This laboratory experiment uses the difference in chemical properties of Fe^{2+}, iron(II), and Fe^{3+}, iron(III), to quantify the amount of each present in a solution of unknown concentrations of each. You will first determine the amount of iron(II) in your sample by titrating with a reagent that does not react with iron(III). You will then titrate a second sample after converting all the iron(III) to iron(II) in order to determine the total iron present. The percent composition of Fe^{2+} in the unknown mixture will be calculated.

BACKGROUND

The concentrations of both iron(II) and iron(III) ions in a solution can be determined by titration with potassium permanganate. The reaction is an oxidation-reduction reaction, or redox, for short. A brief introduction to oxidation-reduction reactions is given in the background of the "Acids and Bases" experiment. The permanganate ion effectively oxidizes iron(II) to iron(III) in an acidic solution while being reduced to manganese(II) ion. The balanced net ionic reaction is:

$$5\ Fe^{2+}(aq) + MnO_4^-(aq) + 8\ H^+(aq) \rightarrow 5\ Fe^{3+}(aq) + Mn^{2+}(aq) + 4\ H_2O(l)$$

Iron(III) is not oxidized by the permanganate ion, and thus does not react. Thus in order to determine the concentration of iron(III) ions, they must first be reduced to iron(II) ions. Zinc metal is used as the reducing agent, also under acidic conditions.

$$Zn(s) + 2\ Fe^{3+}(aq) \rightarrow 2\ Fe^{2+}(aq) + Zn^{2+}(aq) \qquad \text{(reduction of the } Fe^{3+})$$

$$Zn(s) + 2\ H^+(aq) \rightarrow Zn^{2+}(aq) + H_2(g) \qquad \text{(a side reaction that oxidizes excess Zn)}$$

The Zn^{2+} formed does not interfere with the subsequent titration because Zn^{2+} is not oxidized by permanganate. Notice that converting all the iron(III) to iron(II) means that the total iron concentration ($[Fe^{2+}] + [Fe^{3+}]$) is titrated, not just the iron(II) originally present.

Techniques

This is a lab will utilize several of the techniques introduced in the experiment "Laboratory Techniques and Measurements," the procedures for which are given in Appendix B. Poor laboratory technique and misuse of the glassware will result in poor data results, which will affect the grade you receive on the laboratory report. In order to use your time efficiently in lab, review how to properly:

rinse glassware	prepare a standard solution	use a volumetric pipette
weigh by difference	set up and use a burette	use a graduated cylinder
heat samples on a hot plate		

Analysis of Iron by Oxidation-Reduction Titration

This lab uses the common quantitative technique of titration. The only difference between the titration you will be doing in this lab and that done in the Molar Mass of a Known Acid lab is the type of reaction used: this lab will use a redox reaction in place of the acid-base reaction performed in the previous experiment.

In order to determine the concentrations of iron(II) and iron(III) ions in a solution containing both ions, two portions of the same sample must be titrated separately. This first titration will determine only the iron(II) concentration. A second sample will be treated with zinc metal in order to reduce the iron(III) to iron(II). The resulting solution will be titrated with potassium permanganate. The result of this titration will give the total iron concentration in the sample. The difference between the first and second titration is the equal to the iron(III) concentration.

In this titration, potassium permanganate serves as its own indicator. The intense purple color of the permanganate solution becomes colorless when the permanganate is reduced to manganese(II). Thus, as iron(II) is oxidized with the addition of the permanganate solution from the burette it will impart a purple color that will fade. However, once there is no iron(II) left in solution a faint purple color will remain, marking the endpoint of the titration. This color can be slightly altered by the presence of iron(III), which is yellow in solution. Remember that iron(III) is generated by the reaction between iron(II) with permanganate, increasing the yellow appearance of the solution and which can interfere with the detection of the endpoint. Phosphoric acid is added to help minimize this effect.

PROCEDURE CITATION

Begin your data and observations section for this experiment with a citation for the procedure you will follow.

PROCEDURE

Most of the data you record in this lab will consist of numerical measurements, though you will also make some qualitative observations as well. You will do two titrations of the solution that have been treated with zinc, and two that have not been treated with zinc.

As you perform this experiment, make a note of all the equipment and chemicals you use. Be sure to include the size of all volumetric glassware and give a description of all the reagents you use.

Part A: Set Up

1. Put about 50 mL of the $KMnO_4$ solution in a clean dry beaker.

2. Rinse a burette (Appendix B) with white markings with the $KMnO_4$ solution.

3. Clamp the burette in a spring-loaded burette clamp and place a waste beaker below it.

4. Fill the burette with the $KMnO_4$ solution using a clean funnel. Follow the remaining guidelines as provided in Appendix B to prepare it for dispensing this solution.

   - Note that a portion of the credit you receive for your burette data will depend on reading it correctly and making appropriate initial and final readings.

5. Your TA will assign either a known or unknown iron solution to you. Acquire approximately 100 mL of your assigned solution in a clean dry beaker. Rinse a 10.00 mL volumetric pipette with the solution twice, discarding the rinse solution in a waste beaker.

   - NOTE: It is important to exclude air from the sample as much as possible since the oxygen in the air can oxidize iron(II) to iron(III). Keep all containers it is in covered with foil and do not stir or shake the sample unless directed to in the procedure.

6. Pipette TWO aliquots of your iron solution into each of four clean 250 mL Erlenmeyer flasks. (20.00 mL of sample in each flask)

7. Use a graduated cylinder to add 10 mL of 3 M sulfuric acid to each flask.

Part B: Reduction of Iron

8. Add one scoop full (about 0.4 - 0.5 g) of zinc metal to *two* of the four flasks. Swirl the contents of these flasks for about 15 minutes.

9. Gently heat the flasks with zinc on a hot plate until all of the zinc metal has reacted. This process may take a long time, so proceed to part C with your other two (non-zinc) flasks while you are waiting for all of the zinc to react.

10. After the zinc has reacted, carefully remove the flasks from the hotplate and let it cool. Once cooled, complete part C with these two flasks.

Part C: Titration of Iron Solutions

11. Use a graduated cylinder to add 10 mL of 8.5 % phosphoric acid to each flask you will titrate.

12. Titrate each flask with the $KMnO_4$ solution from the burette. As you do this, swirl the flask gently. The endpoint of this titration is when the solution in the flask turns and stays a faint purple color.

Part D: More Data

13. Wash out your four flasks and set them up again as you did in part A, then repeat parts B and C. This is so you will have enough data to work with.

14. When you are done, enter all your data into the Excel program titled "Analysis of Iron."

15. This program will calculate iron concentrations for your solutions for you, but you will still have to demonstrate at least two calculations in the calculations section.

Part E: Clean-up

16. Dispose of all remaining solutions in the waste container in the fume hood.

17. Wash all glassware with detergent, rinse thoroughly with water, and place on your towel to dry.

18. Clean-up all spills and throw all garbage in the garbage cans.

Part F: Collaborator Data

19. If you were assigned an unknown iron solution, collect the following data from someone who was assigned a known solution. If you were assigned a known, collect the same from someone who was assigned an unknown:

  - The average iron (II) concentration present in the non-reduced flasks (the ones that did not have zinc added to them).

  - The standard deviation of the iron (II) concentrations from the non-reduced flasks.

  - The average iron (II) concentration present in the reduced flasks (the ones to which zinc was added.)

  - The standard deviation of the iron (II) concentrations from the reduced flasks.

  - The composition of the known iron solution (if you did not have it already).

POST-LAB: CALCULATIONS
Perform the following calculations on your data, not your collaborator's

1. Use data from two of your trials to calculate the molarity of Fe^{2+} in that sample. One of these trials must be from a non-reduced sample of iron solution, the other from a reduced sample.

2. Average the four concentrations of Fe^{2+} from the trials performed with the non-reduced flasks. You may use the four concentrations your computer calculated for you in lab for this (if you did not write these down, you will have to calculate the concentration of each trial separately, then average them).

3. Calculate the standard deviation of the four concentrations of Fe^{2+} from the non-reduced flasks. You must do the calculation; do not just report the number your computer gave you.

4. Calculate the range this standard deviation falls around its associated average by adding one standard deviation to the average and subtracting one from it.

5. Average the four concentrations of Fe^{2+} from the trials performed with the reduced flasks (the "with zinc" flasks).

6. Calculate the standard deviation of the four concentrations of Fe^{2+} from the reduced flasks.

7. Calculate the range this standard deviation falls around its associated average by adding one standard deviation to the average and subtracting one from it.

Perform the following calculation on your collaborator's data

8. Calculate the range the non-reduced flask concentration standard deviation falls around its associated average by adding one standard deviation to the average and subtracting one from it.

9. Calculate the range the reduced flask concentration standard deviation falls around its associated average by adding one standard deviation to the average and subtracting one from it.

10. Calculate the percent composition of your collaborator's iron solution as you did for your own. (That is, by calculating two percentages to obtain a range.)

POST-LAB: RESULTS AND DISCUSSION
The remaining requirements for your post-lab assignment will either be provided on-line or in a handout.

APPENDIX A: LABORATORY EQUIPMENT

Some of the equipment used in General Chemistry is pictured below. The following page has a detailed description of some of the more commonly used glassware.

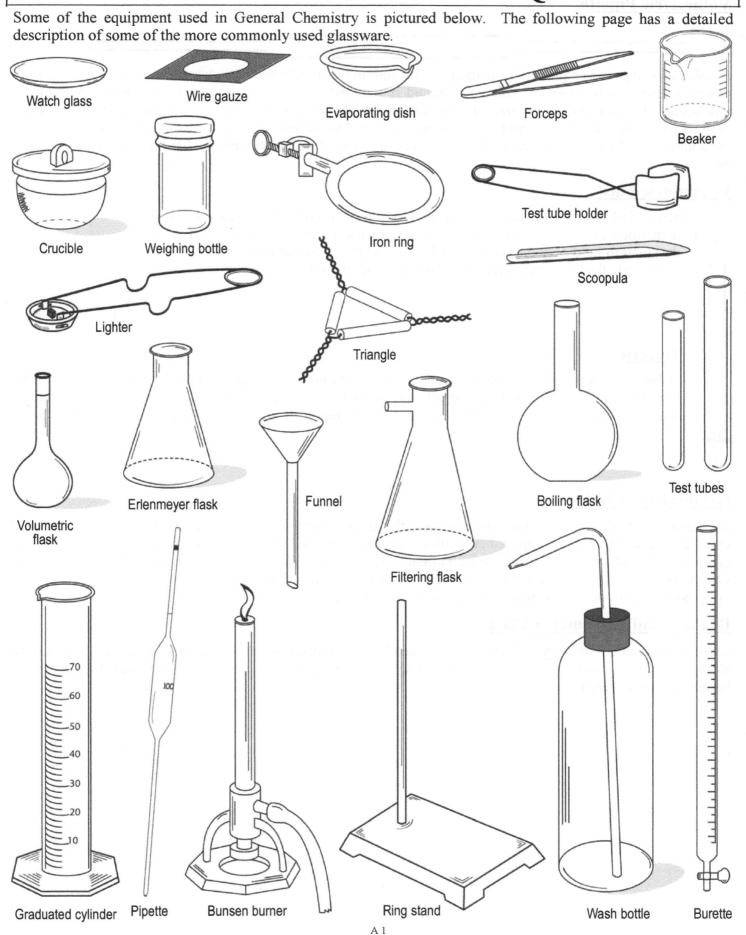

Watch glass

Wire gauze

Evaporating dish

Forceps

Beaker

Crucible

Weighing bottle

Iron ring

Test tube holder

Scoopula

Lighter

Triangle

Volumetric flask

Erlenmeyer flask

Funnel

Filtering flask

Boiling flask

Test tubes

Graduated cylinder Pipette Bunsen burner

Ring stand

Wash bottle Burette

Volumetric Pipette

A volumetric pipette is a glass tube, usually with a bulb in the middle and an index mark on the upper stem. A pipette is used when a specific volume of liquid is required and must be accurately measured. Volumetric pipettes are available in different sizes that are designed to deliver only one specific volume; this volume will be marked on the pipette. In this course, if you are instructed to use one of these to dispense a volume of liquid, the amount you dispense will be equal to that of your pipette. A volumetric pipette has an uncertainty of ± 0.01 mL.

Volumetric Flask

A volumetric flask is a flask with a narrow neck designed to contain a given volume of liquid when filled to an index mark. Like the volumetric pipette, a volumetric flask is designed to hold only one volume of liquid, and thus they come in many sizes. A volumetric flask has an uncertainty of 0.1% of their total volume.

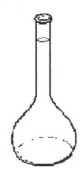

Burette

A burette is a glass tube with a stopcock, a tip on its lower end, and calibration marks along the tube. The burette is used when the actual volume delivered, rather than a specific volume needed, is measured. In this class, you will be using 25.00 mL burettes, which have an uncertainty of ± 0.01 mL.

Graduated Cylinder

A graduated cylinder is a glass tube standing on a flared base with calibration marks along the tube. Graduated cylinders are used when an approximate volume of liquid is needed because the uncertainty on a graduated cylinder is 5% of the maximum cylinder volume. The smallest graduated cylinder that will hold the entire volume being measured should always be used. For example, if you are measuring 40 mL of liquid, use a 50 mL graduated cylinder rather than a 100 mL or a 25 mL twice.

Beakers and Erlenmeyer Flasks

Some beakers and Erlenmeyer flasks have graduations marked on them. These graduations are accurate to about 20% and are only useful for crude estimates. Beakers and Erlenmeyer flasks are used for containing liquids, not measuring them.

APPENDIX B
LABORATORY TECHNIQUES

CLEANLINESS

A fundamental part of good laboratory technique, in any type of laboratory, is preventing contamination. Here are a few rules you and all of your classmates need to observe.

- Use only the dropper or spatula that is with a reagent bottle. Never dip any personal stir rod, Pasteur pipette, spatula, etc. into a reagent bottle.

- Do not touch the dispensing dropper or spatula to the sides of your glassware.

- Keep the lids on all reagent bottles.

- Never lay clean pipettes, stirring rods, or reagent droppers on the benchtop where they could become contaminated.

- Never return unused reagent or solid salts to the stock bottles.

- Use a clean pipette every time you work with a new sample.

- To clean glassware, first dispose of remaining solution into the waste container or as instructed. Then rinse thoroughly with tap water. Scrub the glassware with the cleaning solution located at all of the sinks. Finally, rinse all your glassware with deionized water and let it air dry.

RINSING GLASSWARE

In order to avoid dilution of a solution by any residual water left on the inside of glassware, the glassware must always be rinsed with the solution it will contain. This process removes the water without trying to tediously dry the glassware. Place a small amount (about 15-20% of the piece's total volume) of the solution in the piece of glassware to be rinsed. Slowly tilt and rotate the piece of glassware so that every inside surface is coated by the solution. Discard this rinse solution. Repeat one time before filling this piece of glassware with the solution it will hold.

OBSERVING ODORS

To note a smell in the lab, you should carefully waft the odor toward your nose.

Never hold a sample under your nose and directly inhale the odor.

MIXING SOLUTIONS IN A TEST TUBE

Though it may seem intuitive to use a stir-rod to mix samples, this can actually be undesirable as it can lead to cross-contamination of your samples. Instead, solutions will be mixed by a technique called "vortexing." To vortex a sample, lightly hold the tube by the top with one hand. With your other hand, lightly thump or tap the lower half of the tube several times. This should cause the solution to swirl in a vortex pattern (like water going down a drain) and adequately mix the solution.

You should be aware that it can sometimes be difficult to mix the contents of smaller test tubes with this technique. If you look closely at your tubes after you add one reagent to another, you may find that they exhibit layers of unmixed solution. Unless you are told in the procedure otherwise (some procedures will require you to layer solutions), always inspect your tubes closely to ensure that their contents are fully mixed when you add reagents together.

TESTING A SOLUTION WITH LITMUS PAPER

Some of your solutions will need to be tested with litmus paper to determine whether they are basic or acidic. The proper method to do this is to dip a clean stirring rod into the solution and then touch the stirring rod to the litmus paper. This will prevent contamination that will occur if the paper itself is dipped into the solution.

Acids turn blue litmus red and bases turn red litmus blue. If a solution was applied to a piece of red litmus paper and the solution did not change color, the solution is either acidic or neutral. However, this information could not be used to distinguish between an acidic or neutral solution because it would not be known if the solution "turned" red or stayed red. A similar situation exists in cases where blue litmus paper does not change color. Into itself, it only tells you that the solution is either basic or neutral.

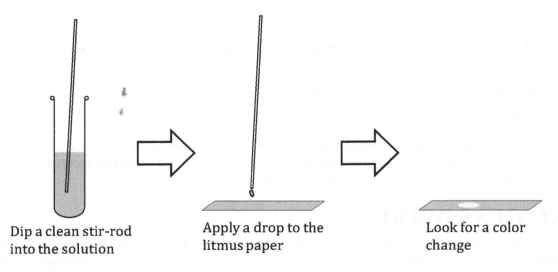

Dip a clean stir-rod into the solution

Apply a drop to the litmus paper

Look for a color change

TESTING FOR AN ACIDC OR BASIC GAS

If the reaction between two chemicals produces a gas, litmus paper can also be used to determine whether that gas is acidic or basic. This can be done by performing the reaction in an enclosed vessel with moistened litmus paper above it:

1. Moisten a piece of red litmus paper and a piece of blue litmus paper with DI water and stick them to the bottom (convex) side of a watch glass.

2. Invert the watch glass and place it on top of an evaporating dish that contains one of the two chemicals you are working with (if one of your two chemicals is a solid, the solid will be in the evaporating dish). The watch glass will act as a kind of lid for the dish.

3. Lift the watch glass, add the other chemical (this will usually be a liquid or an aqueous solution) to the dish, and quickly replace the watch glass.

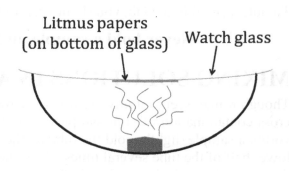

Litmus papers (on bottom of glass)   Watch glass

As the reaction progresses, vapors from it will come into contact with the litmus paper. If those vapors are acidic, the blue litmus paper will turn red. If the vapors are basic, the red litmus paper will turn blue.

HEATING SAMPLES

In this course, you will use a hot water bath to heat your samples instead of an open flame. To setup and use one of these:

- Place your hotplate under your benchtop fume hood.

- Put about 200 mL of deionized water and 2 or 3 boiling chips in a 250 mL beaker.

  o Note: deionized water must be used for this to prevent scale build-up.

- Place the beaker on the hotplate and initially turn the hotplate to a mid-range (5 or 6) setting.

- Increase the temperature one setting if the water is not boiling after about five minutes. Continue to increase the temperature setting every few minutes until the water is just boiling.

- The water should only simmer, not be at a "roiling boil".

- To heat small test tubes, place a small rubber band around the top of the test tubes and set them in the holes of an aluminum plate placed on top of the beaker. Large test tubes are heated by placing them in the hot water bath without the plate.

- Check your hot water bath periodically throughout the laboratory class and add more deionized water as needed. Do not let it boil dry.

DECANTING

Decanting is the process of separating a precipitate from a solution. To help distinguish it from the solid precipitate, liquid solution is commonly called the supernatant.

- The precipitate must be well settled and the solution above it clear. (Cloudiness is the result of suspended precipitate in the solution.)

- Once the precipitate has settled to the bottom of the beaker or test tube, gently and SLOWLY pour the solution from the top into another beaker or test tube without disturbing the settled precipitate.

- Continue tipping the beaker until nearly all the solution has been removed and transferring some precipitate with the supernatant cannot be avoided. Some solution will be left with the precipitate.

NUMERICAL DATA

Much of the numerical data that you will collect in this course will consist of figures that are read off glassware, balances or other instruments. In order to properly collect these data, it is important that you understand how many digits you are supposed to record, and how to properly read your glassware. Some of your data will be provided on a digital display that will allow you to read and record the number directly. In the case of glassware, however, you will have to learn to "read" the glassware and determine for yourself what number to record and how many digits to record it to.

Reading a Meniscus

Reading glassware mostly consists of determining where the level of the fluid in it is relative to its markings, which are sometimes called "index marks." To do this properly, you need to be able to interpolate between the markings. For example, consider the magnified image of a graduated cylinder that contains an amount of water (next page). This particular cylinder has markings that read to the tenths place; that is, they are in increments of 0.1 mL. Notice that the surface of the water in the cylinder is not flat, but curves upward around the edge to form what is called a meniscus. Also note that the meniscus is not a thin line, but appears as a band of noticeable thickness.

The level of the liquid is measured by comparing the *bottom* of the meniscus with the cylinder's index marks. Though these markings are only to the tenths place, by properly interpolating between them it is possible to read the fluid level to the hundredths place (nearest 0.01 mL). Since the meniscus is halfway, or perhaps a little more than halfway, between 6.5 mL and 6.6 mL, we might read it as either 6.55 or maybe 6.56 mL.

As a general rule, the digit you measure by interpolation will be 1/10 the value of the index markings. In this case, the markings were in 0.1 mL increments, so we interpolate to the nearest 0.01 mL.

As you will discover in lab, reading these can be difficult at first and takes some practice. It is worth noting that interpolation is, to an extent, subject to interpretation; therefore, it will not provide an absolutely "right" value. It is important, though, that you are consistent in how you take your readings.

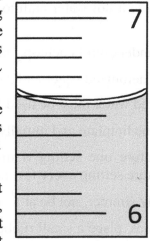

Magnified view of fluid in a graduated cylinder. By interpolating, this fluid can be read as 6.55 mL even though the graduation marks are in increments of 0.1 mL.

Significant Zeros

Whenever you do record a number, it is important that you always do so to the correct number of significant figures. This includes writing down a zero if the last digit in your reading is zero. For example, if the meniscus in a graduated cylinder falls exactly on the 5.1 mL index mark, you would record 5.10 mL, not 5.1 mL. The reason for this is that it lets the person who checks or otherwise has to work with your data know to what precision the measurement was made to; 5.10 mL means the measurement was taken to the hundredths place and is therefore more precise than 5.1 mL. This also holds true with fixed-volume glassware such as the pipette and volumetric flask; a "10 mL" pipette is really a 10.00 mL pipette, so its volume should be recorded as such.

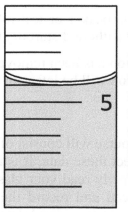

The graduation marks on this cylinder are in increments of 0.1 mL. Therefore, this would be read as 5.10, not simply 5.1 mL

Choosing the right equipment

Because of the differences in accuracy limitations inherent to various types of instruments, it is important that the right one be chosen for any given task. For example, although a common ruler would be useful to measure the length of your hand, it would be highly inappropriate to use it to measure the length of a street or the thickness of a postage stamp. Generally speaking, it is desirable to choose the instrument that will give you the best precision for your task. However, for those times when such precision is not required, use of the more precise instrument may not be worth the effort of using it. Part of becoming competent in a laboratory is recognizing when such precision is, and is not, required.

REAGENT QUANTITIES

Measured Amounts

Many of the experiments described in this manual will instruct you to dispense a certain quantity of solid or liquid reagent. For instance, a step may say "add 5 mL of X," or "weigh out 3 grams of salt." However, these instructions do not mean that you must use exactly the amount of reagent they indicate. Instead, it is implied that you should dispense the indicated quantity give-or-take a certain "tolerance" amount. What this tolerance amount is depends on what you are using to measure the reagent:

- If you are using a piece of volumetric glassware such as a graduated cylinder or a burette, dispense the indicated amount ± 2 index (graduation) marks. If, for instance, you are using a graduated cylinder that has index marks in 0.2 mL increments and you are instructed to dispense 5 mL, it is intended that you dispense something between 4.6 mL and 5.4 mL. This rule does not apply to non-volumetric glassware such as a beaker.

- If you are using a balance, dispense the targeted amount ±10%. For example, if you are instructed to dispense 3 grams, you may dispense anything between 2.7 g and 3.3 g.

Be aware that, as for all numerical data, what you record in your manual will be worth points in your data section. If the quantities you record in your notes all exactly equal the quantities indicated in the manual, your figures will be called into question and you may lose points.

Also be aware that there is one piece of volumetric glassware you will work with that these instructions do not apply to: the volumetric pipette. Volumetric pipettes must always be used to dispense exactly the amount of fluid they were designed to.

Approximated Amounts

There will be times during some of your experiments when it is permissible to use an approximate amount of a reagent, as opposed to a carefully metered, measured amount. This will enable you to save time in lab and work a little more efficiently. The following approximations may help you in this regard. When you use one of these, be sure to report how you approximated the quantity you used.

- Approximately 20 drops from a Pasteur pipette is equal to 1 mL of solution.
- Small test tubes hold between 4 and 5 mL.

A spatula tip full of solid is about the size of a small pea.

TOP LOADING BALANCE

The top loading balances used in General Chemistry give a digital reading to the nearest 0.001 g. All three decimals are recorded, even if they are zeroes. The top loading balance has an uncertainty of ±0.001 g. When using the top loading balances follow these guidelines.

- Check that the balance is level. Many balances have a bubble-type level on them for this purpose.
- Be sure the balance reads zero with nothing on the pan and the cover on before weighing a sample. Press the "tare" button if it does not.
- Close the cover on the balance when taking a mass measurement, but be sure it does not rest on the sample or the sample container.
- Do not place samples directly on the balance pan at anytime. Always use a weighing bottle.

- Use the same balance for a series of mass measurements, particularly when weighing by difference.

- Make sure the sample is at room temperature before taking its mass because convection currents will cause unstable readings.

- Do not weigh wet or damp samples because evaporation makes it difficult to obtain a stable reading. Furthermore, moisture increases the apparent mass of the sample. Moisture can also lead to unwanted corrosion of the balance pan.

- Do not place heavy glassware, such as beakers, on the balances.

- Never bring a reagent bottle to the balance area.

- Always bring your lab notebook to the balances and record the mass directly into your notebook.

- Any spills that occur on the balance should be cleaned up immediately. If you need help, ask your TA.

WEIGHING BY DIFFERENCE

Weighing by difference is a method used to transfer a known mass of a sample to a reaction vessel without directly weighing the reaction vessel. This is most often done with solid chemicals.

To weigh-out a reagent by difference, first put some of it into a weighing bottle. Next, weigh the bottle to determine the combined mass of it and its reagent contents. Tip some of the contents out into the vessel to be used in the experiment. To protect the balances from spills, you must perform this transfer at your laboratory workbench instead of the balance area*. Finally, reweigh the bottle and remaining contents. The difference between the mass of the bottle and contents before and after transfer is the mass of the reagent actually used. In the case of the example below, since the mass of the weighing bottle before transfer was 15.707 g and the mass after transfer was 13.351 g, 2.356 g of reagent were transferred into the beaker (the "separate vessel").

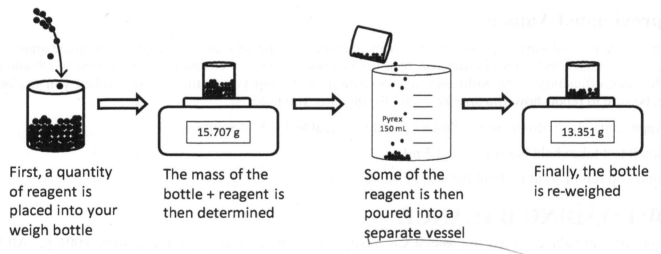

First, a quantity of reagent is placed into your weigh bottle

The mass of the bottle + reagent is then determined

15.707 g

Some of the reagent is then poured into a separate vessel

Pyrex 150 mL

Finally, the bottle is re-weighed

13.351 g

If the difference is less than the mass required for the experiment, transfer more reagent to the reaction vessel and re-weigh the bottle and remaining reagent. Repeat this process until the desired mass of reagent has been transferred to the reaction vessel. Note that it will not be necessary to include the masses of these intermediate "weighings" in your calculations.

If the difference is greater than the maximum mass allowed in the experiment, then the reagent in the vessel must be discarded (Dispose of the material as directed in the clean-up portion of the procedure.) Thoroughly clean and rinse the reaction vessel and repeat the weighing by difference procedure from the beginning. Be certain to transfer less of the reagent this time.

*In this and all other general chemistry courses, no transfers of any kind, including from the reagent bottle to the weighing bottle as well as from the weighing bottle to the reaction vessel, are permitted at the balances. *Violations of this rule will result in point penalties on your lab reports.*

VOLUMETRIC PIPETTE

Volumetric pipettes are glass tubes, usually with a bulb in the middle and an index mark on the upper stem, that are designed to dispense a certain quantity of fluid. They are available in different sizes that each deliver only one specific volume; this volume will be marked on the pipette. In this course, if you are instructed to use one of these to dispense a volume of liquid, the amount you dispense will be equal to that of your pipette. Many of the procedures in this manual will refer to this quantity, one full pipette load, as an "aliquot." A volumetric pipette has an uncertainty of ±0.01 mL. To properly use a pipette:

1. Place a pipette filler or bulb on the top of the tube just enough to get suction. Do not force it; the bulb or pipette filler should be easily removable (you will remove it in a subsequent step), and certain kinds of bulb are actually designed so the pipette cannot be fully inserted into them.

2. Rinse the pipette by using the pump or bulb to draw up the solution you will ultimately dispense in it and let this solution drain into a waste container. Do this three times.

3. Holding the pipette completely vertical and without letting the tip touch the bottom of the container from which the solution is being drawn, pull the liquid up until it is above the index mark.

   - Note: *be careful when the bulb portion of the pipette is nearly full.* Once this is full and the portion above it begins to fill, the level will rise very rapidly. This makes it easy for fluid to shoot all the way up into the vacuum pump or bulb.

4. Remove the bulb or pipette filler and cover the top of the pipette with your finger. This must be done quickly or the liquid will drain below the index mark before you can get your finger over the opening. Carefully let the liquid drain until the meniscus is at the index mark.

5. Hold the pipette over the container the liquid is being transferred to and gravity drain.

   - The pipettes you will use in this course are of the "to deliver" type. This means that they are calibrated to deliver the indicated amount of liquid when they are allowed to gravity drain. A small portion of fluid will remain in the tip, but this is accounted for in the pipette's calibration. For this reason, *you must not "blow out" this last remaining portion of liquid.* Forcing it out will compromise the pipette's accuracy.

6. Touch the last drop hanging from the tip to the inside surface of the container.

   Steps 3, 4, and 5 are depicted in the following diagram.

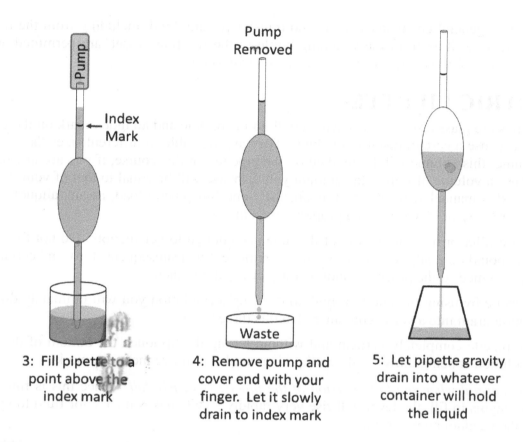

3: Fill pipette to a point above the index mark

4: Remove pump and cover end with your finger. Let it slowly drain to index mark

5: Let pipette gravity drain into whatever container will hold the liquid

BURETTE

Burettes are made for accurate dispensing of variable volumes of liquids. They are especially useful for dispensing fluids when the final desired volume is not known ahead of time, such as during a titration experiment. The following points are imperative to good laboratory technique when using a burette.

1. The burette must be rinsed before use. This is done by adding a portion, about 20% of the burette's capacity will do, of the solution or solvent that will ultimately fill the burette to it, moving the burette around to wash its insides with this solution, and draining it out through the stopcock (the valve at the bottom).

2. To ready the burette for dispensing, fill it to a point above the 0.00 mL mark. Open the stopcock and allow it to drain to a point below the 0.00 mL mark. This is done to ensure the tip is filled with fluid and all the air has been purged from it. Draining it down to exactly the 0.00 mL mark is an unnecessary waste of time and is considered improper. Check the tip when you are done to ensure it has been fully purged of air. Wipe the tip to remove any drops hanging from it.

3. Since the burette's markings are to the tenths (0.X) place, readings are made to the hundredths (0.0X) place. As there are no hundredths place markings, this digit is determined by interpolation (described above). It is worth noting that the burette's markings are "upside down" relative to how they are on a graduated cylinder. For example, consider the "initial" burette in the diagram below. Notice that the 6 is above the 7. This meniscus would therefore be read as 6.39 mL, or possibly 6.38 mL.

4. To dispense a volume from the burette, first make initial meniscus reading. Open the stopcock until the desired volume has been dispensed, then read the meniscus again. Subtract the final reading from the initial to calculate the amount added. As the initial reading cannot be 0.00 mL, the final cannot be 25.00 (or whatever the burette's maximum volume is). This is because a burette can only be accurately read between the markings. During use, the last drop will often hang from the tip. Since this drop is part of the measured volume it must be added to the container by touching it to the side of the receiving vessel.

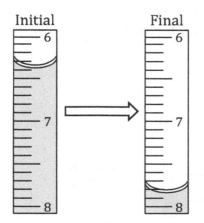

Initial   Final

In this example, the person has been instructed to dispense 1.5 mL

The initial volume is 6.39 and the final volume is 7.85, so the actual amount dispensed is 1.46 mL. This is perfectly acceptable.

- For full credit in your experiments, all burette data must consist of an initial and a final reading. A single number that represents the volume dispensed is meaningless.

- You will also not receive full credit if all of your readings are to the nearest whole mL (e.g., 1.00, 2.00, 3.00, etc.), even if you record your data to the correct number of significant figures. This is simply because having all of your readings come out this way is sufficiently unlikely that, for all practical purposes, it does not happen if you are using the burette correctly.

5. The burettes you will use in this course all have index marks in increments of 0.1 mL. Therefore, when you use a burette to dispense a certain amount of liquid, the actual amount you dispense may be anything that is 0.2 mL less than or greater than what you were directed to dispense. For example, if the amount you "should" use is nominally 5 mL, you may actually dispense anything between 4.8 and 5.2 mL. As for all measured reagent quantities, it is a waste of time to try to use the burettes to dispense an exact amount of liquid.

STANDARD SOLUTIONS & THE VOLUMETRIC FLASK

Stock solutions are solutions that have an accurately known concentration. To ensure this accuracy, they are commonly made in a volumetric flask. To make such a solution when starting with a solid (i.e., "dry") substance:

1. First, clean your flask and rinse it with the solvent you will be using. (With rare exceptions, the solvent will always be water, so rinse it with DI water.)

2. Use the "weigh by difference" technique to transfer the desired amount of solid into an appropriately-sized beaker. In this case, "appropriately-sized" means something at least larger than half the flask's volume.

3. Dissolve the solid in a quantity of solvent large enough to bring all of it into solution, but less than the volume of the volumetric flask. About 1/3 of the volume of the flask is a good go-to volume for this.

4. Use a funnel to pour the dissolved solid solution down a stir rod directed at the funnel in the volumetric flask. This prevents splashing and loss of solution.

5. Use a wash bottle filled with solvent to rinse the sides of the beaker while it is tipped over the funnel. Wash the beaker in this way until the flask is between half and 2/3 full.

6. Rinse the stir rod and funnel into the flask. Avoid leaving drops of solvent above the index mark on the inside the volumetric flask. Wash such drops down below the mark.

7. Fill the volumetric to the index line with solvent, being very careful not to overshoot. As you near the mark, add only a drop of solvent at a time with a dropper or wash bottle. If you overshoot, you must dispose of the solution, clean and rinse the volumetric flask, and start the whole process over.

8. Stopper the volumetric flask. Invert the flask 20-30 times to mix. If solution leaks out, dispose of the solution, clean and rinse the volumetric flask, and start the whole process over.

These steps are summarized in the following diagram.

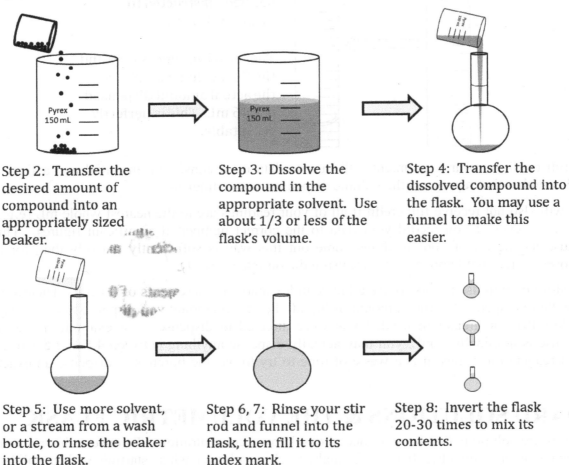

Step 2: Transfer the desired amount of compound into an appropriately sized beaker.

Step 3: Dissolve the compound in the appropriate solvent. Use about 1/3 or less of the flask's volume.

Step 4: Transfer the dissolved compound into the flask. You may use a funnel to make this easier.

Step 5: Use more solvent, or a stream from a wash bottle, to rinse the beaker into the flask.

Step 6, 7: Rinse your stir rod and funnel into the flask, then fill it to its index mark.

Step 8: Invert the flask 20-30 times to mix its contents.

In addition to being used to make a stock solution from a dry chemical, volumetric flasks can also be used to dilute already-made stock solutions. In this case, you would use a pipette or burette to dispense a portion of the solution to be dissolved into the flask, then fill the flask to its index mark with solvent. The amount you add to the flask would depend on how much you wanted to dilute the solution by and the size of the flask.

Volume by Displacement

Volume by displacement is often used to find the volume of a solid object (See figure "Volume by Displacement"). The first step is to fill a graduated cylinder with some liquid (often water) and read the volume. The exact amount of liquid present is unimportant as long as it is enough to completely cover the object. Next, carefully slide the object into the cylinder and take another volume reading. The volume of liquid displaced by the object (i.e., the difference between the two readings) is equal to the volume of the object.

- You will generally use this technique to determine the volume of metal slugs in this course. The 10 mL graduated cylinders will work best for this.

- When you insert the slug, tilt the graduated cylinder so the slug slides in; don't drop it in.

- The amount of water you place in the cylinder should be sufficient to completely cover the slug (so you may need more than 1.6 mL).

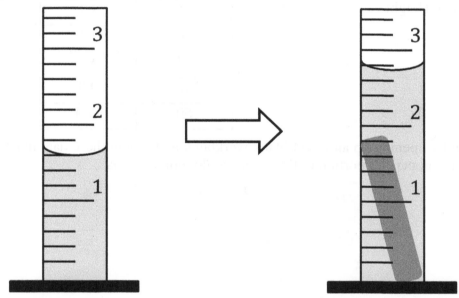

First, an amount of water is placed into a graduated cylinder. In this case, the level would be read and recorded as 1.60 mL

The object being measured is then inserted into the cylinder and the new water level noted. Since the new level is 2.72 mL, and the original was 1.60 mL, this object has a volume of 1.12 mL

Volume by Displacement

EXCEL OPERATIONS, 2007-2010 VERSIONS

The following instructions are for the 2007 and 2010 versions of Excel. If you have Excel 2013 or 2016, see the alternate instructions for the 2013-2016 version.

Making a Chart in Excel

The following information will assist you in making a data plot; that is, a graphical representation of your data that allows two sets of numbers to be compared to each other to see if there is any relationship between them. We will do this by re-creating the Plant Height vs. Age chart that appears in the Laboratory Report Guidelines chapter.

The data points in the Plant Height vs. Age chart are in the table to the right.

Age (days)	Height (cm)
10	2.6
18	4.1
26	7.1
34	8.3
42	9.8
50	12.4

Begin your plot creation by opening up an Excel blank workbook and typing these data into columns A and B. When you are finished, the upper-left portion of the sheet should look like this:

When you are done entering these numbers, select the cells they are in by clicking on cell A1, holding the mouse button down, and dragging it to cell B6. Alternatively, you can select cell A1, hold down the shift key, and use the arrow keys to move down and right to cell B6. All of the cells the numbers are in, except possibly the upper-left most cell, should be shaded when you are done.

When the cells are selected, go into the "Insert" portion of the ribbon (the line of menu options at the top of the page). Within the insert portion, you should see a section titled "Charts." This section contains options for a wide variety of different kinds of charts you can make a group of data into, including column, line, and pie charts. The one we will use is a "scatter" chart.

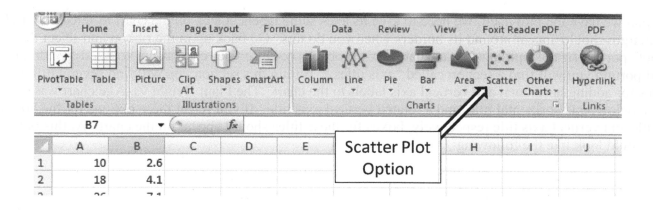

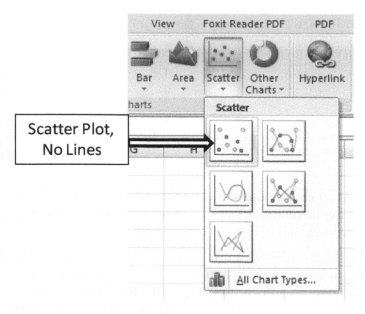

Within the scatter chart menu, you will find several different sub-types of scatter plots, such as "scatter", "scatter with smooth lines and markers," and "scatter with straight lines". The plot we are trying to create is a "scatter" plot (with markers only, no lines), so select this one.

Excel should create a chart that looks like the following; if your chart is blank, it's because you didn't select any data for it. Later on (not now), you should try some of the other scatter-plot options (scatter with smooth lines, etc.) so you can see the differences between them.

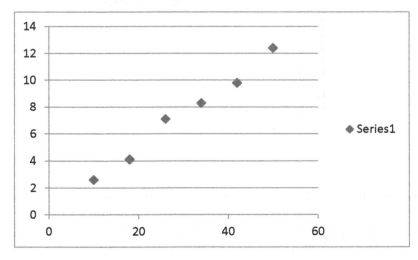

Note that the data in column A has been placed on the X (horizontal) axis and the data in column B has been placed on the Y (vertical) axis.

The notation "◆Series1" to the right of the plot is a key to let the reader know which series of numbers correspond to the makers with a "◆" shape; it's really only useful for charts that have multiple series of numbers in them. You can delete it for the plot we are creating.

Now that we have the plot itself, we need to give its axes some labels. Click on the chart to select it; a light-gray margin should appear around its borders when you do this. Go back up to the ribbon and select the "layout" portion (if this option is not available, it's probably because your chart is not selected). Within the layout portion you will find a section called "axis titles." Within this section you will find several different options for adding horizontal and vertical axis labels to the chart. The Plant Height vs. Age chart was created using a below-axis horizontal title, and a rotated vertical axis title. If you select these options for the horizontal axis title and vertical axis title respectively, boxes for these titles should appear on the chart. At this point, the chart should look like the following:

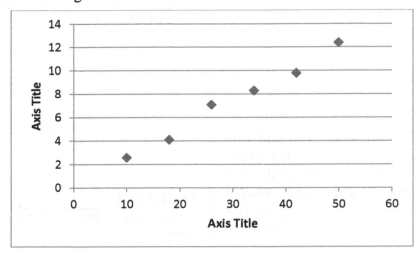

You can change the names of the individual axis titles by selecting them, deleting the text "Axis Title" and re-naming them appropriately. In the Plant Height vs. Age chart, the horizontal axis is labeled "Age (days)" and the vertical axis "Height (centimeters)".

Finally, we will put a title on the chart. This can be added similarly to the way the individual axis titles were added. First, select "chart title" from the layout portion of the ribbon. You will be given options to add the title as an overlay title, or to put it above the chart. The two examples below depict what the Plant Height chart we are creating would look like with the "above chart" option on the left, and the "overlay" option on the right. Placing the title above the plot generally looks neater, though it also makes the plot more compact.

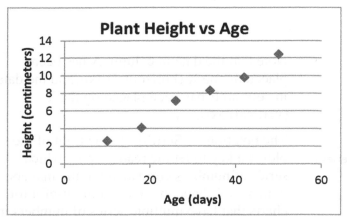

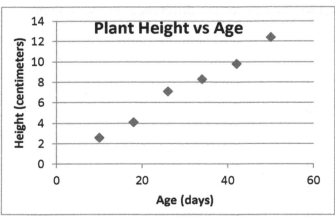

The original Plant Height vs Age chart also contains one other feature that our current chart so-far does not: a best-fit line through its data points. As a general rule, you will be asked to draw these by hand on a printed copy of your chart if your chart is required to have one. However, if you want to have Excel draw one of these, you will find the options for adding a best-fit line in the "Trendline" portion of the Layout section of the ribbon.

Math Operations in Excel

Math Operations in the 2007 and 2010 versions of Excel are not substantially different from those in the 2013 and 2016 editions. See the equivalent section in the instructions for 2013/2016 Excel for information on these.

EXCEL OPERATIONS, 2013-2016 VERSIONS

The following instructions are for the 2013 and 2016 versions of Excel. If you have Excel 2007 or 2010, see the alternate instructions for the 2007-2010 version.

Making a Chart in Excel

The following information will assist you in making a data plot; that is, a graphical representation of your data that allows two sets of numbers to be compared to each other to see if there is any relationship between them. We will do this by re-creating the Plant Height vs. Age chart that appears in the Laboratory Report Guidelines chapter.

The data points in the Plant Height vs. Age chart are in the table to the right.

Age (days)	Height (cm)
10	2.6
18	4.1
26	7.1
34	8.3
42	9.8
50	12.4

Begin your plot creation by opening up an Excel blank workbook and typing these data into columns A and B. When you are finished, the upper-left portion of the sheet should look like this:

	A	B	C	D	E
1	10	2.6			
2	18	4.1			
3	26	7.1			
4	34	8.3			
5	42	9.8			
6	50	12.4			
7					
8					

When you are done entering these numbers, select the cells they are in by clicking on cell A1, holding the mouse button down, and dragging it to cell B6. Alternatively, you can select cell A1, hold down the shift key, and use the arrow keys to move down and right to cell B6. All of the cells the numbers are in, except possibly the upper-left most cell, should be shaded when you are done.

When the cells are selected, go into the "Insert" portion of the ribbon (the line of menu options at the top of the page). Within the insert portion, you should see a section titled "Charts." This section contains options for a wide variety of different kinds of charts you can make a group of data into, including column, line, and pie charts. The one we will use is a "scatter" chart.

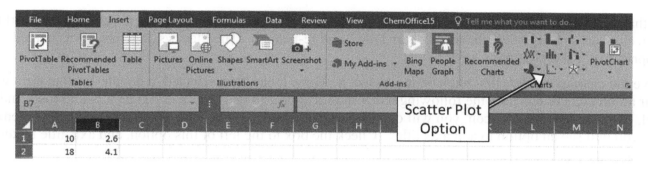

Within the scatter chart menu, you will find several different sub-types of scatter plots, such as "scatter", "scatter with smooth lines and markers," and "scatter with straight lines". The plot we are trying to create is a "scatter" plot (with markers only, no lines), so select this one.

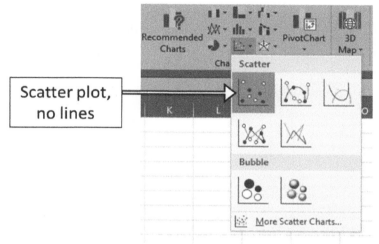

On some versions of Excel for Apple computers, you will find the chart options in its own tab at the top of the worksheet. The options for scatter plots are in this tab.

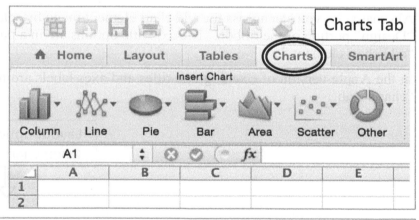

Excel should create a chart that looks like the following; if your chart is blank, it's because you didn't select any data for it. Note that the data in column A has been placed on the X (horizontal) axis and the data in column B has been placed on the Y (vertical) axis. Later on (not now), you should try some of the other scatter-plot options (scatter with smooth lines, etc.) so you can see the differences between them.

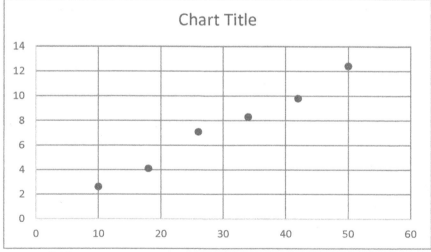

Now that we have the plot itself, we can modify its title and give it some axes labels. To change the chart title, simply click on its box, delete the text "Chart Title," and re-name it. The Plant vs. Age chart was named, appropriately, "Plant Height vs Age."

To give the chart axis titles, first click on it to select it. Once it has been selected, a double-lined margin will appear around its borders, and the following icons should appear to its right: a "+" sign, a paint brush, and a funnel. If you select the "+" icon, you will open the "add chart element" menu. Within the add chart element menu, you will see an option to add axis titles. Check the box to the left of this option, and axis title boxes will appear on the chart:

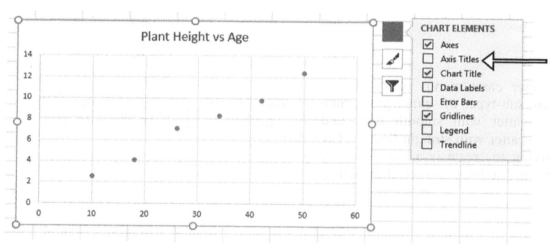

Alternatively, you can access the add chart element menu by selecting the chart as described, then going into the "Design" portion of the ribbon. The axis title options are in a pull-down menu that appears when you select "add chart element."

In the Apple version of Excel, graph titles and axes labels are found in the "chart layout" tab, right next to the "charts" tab:

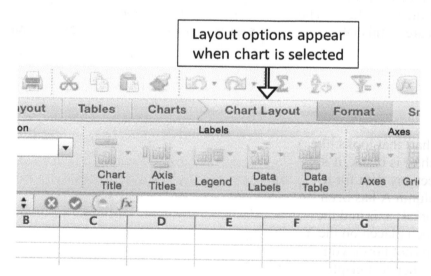

You can change the names of the individual axis titles by selecting them, deleting the text "Axis Title" and renaming them appropriately. In the Plant Height vs. Age chart, the horizontal axis is labeled "Age (days)" and the vertical axis "Height (centimeters)".

The original Plant Height vs Age chart also contains one other feature that our current chart so-far does not: a best-fit line through its data points. As a general rule, you will be asked to draw these by hand on a printed copy of your chart if your chart is required to have one. However, if you want to have Excel draw one of these, you will find the options for adding a best-fit line in the "Trendline" portion of the add chart element menu.

Math Operations in Excel

One of the more useful features of Excel, or any other spreadsheet program, is it allows you to perform mathematical operations on a large group of numbers quickly and consistently. For example, let's say instead of days, we wanted to report the times our plants grew in hours. Since there are 24 hours in a day, the numbers of days in the table above can be converted to hours by multiplying each number by 24. Excel can help you do this to every number in the column in just a few steps:

Inserting a Row

First, let's give the columns titles so we can keep track of them easier. If you haven't typed any numbers in yet, you can type the column titles into the row at the top of each column before you put the numbers in. If your numbers are already typed in, however, you'll have to make some room for the titles. You can do this by selecting any cell in row 1 and using the insert row feature in the Home part of the ribbon:

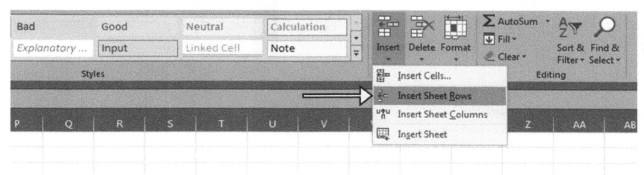

Now that we have a row to type them into, we can give our columns titles. For simplicity, let's call the original age column "days," and the height column "cm." The new column for the plants' ages will be called "hours."

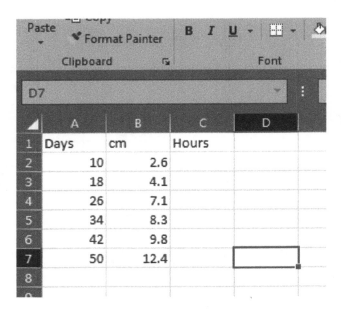

Multiplication and the Fill Handle

The mathematical operation that will give us the plants' ages in hours can now be typed in. Go to the first cell under "Hours," cell C2 in our example, and type =A2*24 . This will tell Excel to multiply the number in cell A2 (10 in this case) by 24:

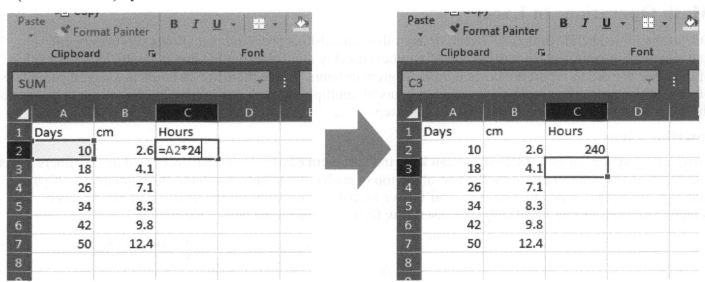

This same operation can be copied to the remaining rows in that column by using the fill handle. Select the cell the formula was just typed into and move the cursor over its bottom-right corner until a solid black cross (+) appears. When it does, hold the mouse key down and drag this cross down to the last row in the table:

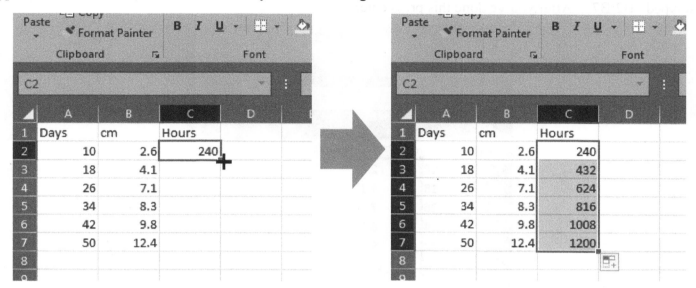

Other Excel Functions

Excel has many different built-in functions you can use to manipulate numbers besides simple multiplication or addition operations. Here we will introduce you to two of them: standard deviation and average.

To use the average function, first click on whatever cell you want the average to appear in and type =average(, but don't press enter yet. If we wanted the average of our plant heights to appear in cell B9, our screen would look like this:

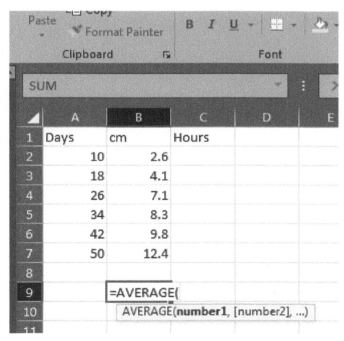

Now we have to tell the function what numbers we want to average. We can do this manually by typing in cell coordinates one by one, or use the click and drag method to highlight the desired cells. In the following picture, we have selected cells B2 through B7 by doing the latter. Instead of clicking and dragging, we could have also just typed B2:B7 . After you've done this press enter:

These same steps can be used to put a standard deviation in another cell, except you will type =stdev.s(in the cell instead of =average(.

Besides average and standard deviation, Excel has hundreds of other pre-programmed functions you may find useful.